From Gasoline to Electric Power

A Conversion Experience

Gary Powers

Bryan Fogg

EVAmerica@aol.com

Electric Vehicles of America, Inc.
Wolfeboro, NH 03894
EVA   *Tel: 603 569-2100*
Fax: 603 569-2115

Longbarn Press
State College, PA

Second Printing, April 2007

ISBN: 0-9660953-0-8

Printed in the United States of America
By Jostens, Inc.

Acknowledgments

A lot of people helped me with this project to convert a pickup truck to electric power. Bob Batson of Electric Vehicles of America was certainly the most instrumental in making this a successful project. Bob has a wealth of experience in the electric vehicle industry and was willing to share his knowledge and skills with someone who began the project knowing virtually nothing about how to get started.

Another big assist came from Kevin Gardner of Gardner's Welding in Watkins Glen, New York. Kevin translated Bob Batson's design and drawings into reality with my truck. Kevin is masterful at innovating a design and fabricating the steel. When I got the truck back from him, it had been transformed into a vehicle ready for new wiring and batteries.

Ev Larson, a longtime friend and co-worker, encouraged me with his constant interest in the project. He also lent valuable help with his woodworking skills and strong arms (lifting the transmission and pushing the truck onto a trailer).

My editor, Laura Morin, made a significant contribution to the book with her many corrections and helpful suggestions (almost all of which I included). She certainly made the book much more readable and enjoyable.

And finally, my wife and son cheerfully allowed me the hours required to convert the truck. My eleven year old son Michael has enjoyed hours of simulated driving in the truck while parked in the garage. So from his perspective, the project was a success even before the batteries were loaded and the truck was on the road. As for my wife, Karen, she has been exploring how to spend as much money on her hobby as I spent on this one.

Gary Powers
July 1997

Contents

Chapter 1

The Decision to Do It

I spent many hours over the past several years converting a 1986 Chevrolet S-10 pickup truck from gasoline to electric power. Before we get into the details of how I converted this truck to electric power, I want to give you some background on how I came to the decision to take on the project. All right, I'll admit this up front – I have an environmentalist viewpoint. I am very concerned about the direction we are headed in our treatment of the air, water, and wilderness. I do not think that we can sustain the current rates of human population growth and material consumption. This will all catch up with us unless we learn to slow down the growth and live with less. I am very confident that we will successfully turn around our consumption and growth habits.

Because of my concern for our environment, I have tried to learn some new habits, with mild success. My family participates in the county recycling program to reduce the amount of trash going to the landfill. We have started to compost garbage, as well, to reduce the amount of trash. Even though my gasoline powered Geo Metro gets forty miles per gallon, I started to consider how to wean myself off the dependency on gasoline. Because others feel the way that I do, I think that the automotive industry will change dramatically in the coming decades. Electric vehicles will become common place. I decided not to wait for the industry to change. Instead, I took on this project as an attempt to learn a new behavior on my own terms rather than holding on to the old paradigm.

The idea came to me as I read more and more about the supposed environmental benefits of driving an electric powered vehicle. I have included some references for you in Appendix E. While one obvious benefit is not having to stop at a gas station for gasoline, my environmental concerns led me to question further benefits. For example, how does the electric utility company generate the electricity for charging the batteries in my electric vehicle? Does it use oil or coal? Why would that be more environmentally friendly than burning gasoline? I realized with the help of Gribben (see Appendix E) that the utility company is more efficient in its use of fossil fuels than my car. Beyond this, I also like the fact that when an electric vehicle is at a stop light or stop sign, it is not using energy. When it is stopped, it is really off – the "engine" is not using any energy at all.

As I considered the project, I wondered if my skills were up to it. To be honest, my background does not make me a good candidate to take on this type of project. Although I have an undergraduate engineering degree, I do not consider myself a real engineer by any stretch of the imagination. There was only one two-year period in my life when I worked as a process engineer in a manufacturing corporation. This was a position that did not require me to design or install any electrical or mechanical equipment. After these two years, I gravitated to less technical positions because I realized that I do not have the mechanical or electrical aptitude to be successful in the engineering world.

In addition, my experience with cars is not a good fit for a conversion project. Sure, I can change the engine oil and oil filter, but with all of the quick lube businesses that also recycle the oil, it is not worth the effort. Beyond this, the extent of my experience in auto repair includes other basic maintenance like changing spark plugs, changing the air filter, changing a flat tire, vacuuming out the inside, and washing the outside (which I try not to do anymore now that my son is eleven years old and he likes to earn money to buy trading cards and play video games). And yet, my desire to do something meaningful to reduce my personal negative impact on the environment far outweighed any evidence of my unsuitability for the project. So if you find yourself in this same position, read on and laugh as you see how this lack of experience is a handicap, but not a show stopper.

At this point I also did not have much information on the safety of electric vehicles. I was so enthusiastic about converting a vehicle that I did not do any research to see if anything was written about the safety considerations. I have since found several references, which are listed for you in Appendix E. One of the references, by the Center for Technology Assessment, is very positive about the safe performance of electric vehicles. The other reference, by the American Petroleum Institute, raises a lot of questions and concerns. This institute, however, has a big stake in the continued success of gasoline powered vehicles.

Like any beginner, I naively entered into this project without a good idea about how much it would cost or how long it would take. Like many things that we all do at home or work that take twice as long and twice as much money as planned, this one would be no different. Except this project would end up costing twice the money and three times as long as I guessed. So I offer this book as an explanation of how I came to be driving a converted Chevy S-10 pickup truck. It is possibly a small warning or a great encouragement for anyone motivated to try a similar project.

Chapter 2

Finding a Company to Help

Real Goods

So, after I had this idea, and had done some reading, I realized I needed more guidance. My search for this help started in the spring of 1994 with a company called Real Goods Trading Corporation in Ukiah, California. This company sells just about anything related to alternative energy use. I had become familiar with this company after receiving their catalog and making some small purchases for the house. Real Good's aim is to provide a means for people to voluntarily "unplug from the grid." They sell items ranging from energy-saving shower heads to complete solar energy packages for a home, and everything in between.

I called them because I was inspired by their 1993 edition of the *Alternative Energy Sourcebook*, which included a section on electric vehicles. This book showed a conversion kit for a Chevy S-10 or GMC S-15 pickup. The description of the kit sounded great and I was ready to dive in. The price also looked pretty good – the kit would only cost about $6000 if I did not want to add solar panels (there isn't much sunlight in upstate New York anyway, where I lived when the conversion began) or re-generative braking (to recover energy when coasting downhill). So I called them to learn more about the conversion kit. As anyone who has taken on such projects knows, it is never this simple. I soon found out that Real Goods no longer offered this kit, but they were happy to put me in touch with the company that manufactured it – Solar Car Corporation of Melbourne, Florida. This was the start of my education about the electric vehicle industry. I did not have any idea that there was so much activity in developing electric vehicles.

While I was on the phone with Real Goods, I placed an order for a copy of the *1993 Worldwide Electric Vehicle Directory*. I thought this would be a good way to find suppliers since I could no longer just call up Real Goods and give them my Visa Card number to get what I might need. This directory turned out to be a great source of information. To my surprise, I found a listing of no fewer than twenty companies in the U.S. alone which, in addition to Solar Car Corporation in Florida, could help me with a conversion. So I decided to contact several of these other companies as well.

California and Florida

I contacted two California companies who do conversions. They sent me their literature in the mail and both of them seemed satisfactory, but I just could not envision doing business with a company that was 3,000 miles away. I was still feeling unsure of my ability to pull off this project, and I felt I needed to work with someone closer to home. Therefore, I decided to concentrate on the east coast, specifically Florida and Massachusetts.

The follow-up with Solar Car Corporation in Florida was very encouraging. I talked with them a total of three times on the phone and they were always very polite, helpful, and supportive. The literature they sent me indicated a pretty solid history of successful conversions. I came very close to ordering their conversion kit, but once again, the long distance discouraged me. I decided to hold off until I contacted the Massachusetts company, the closest company to my location in New York. I grew up in New England, and I suppose I had an emotional need to keep my business close to "home." I was also intrigued by an electric vehicle company in Massachusetts. I expected these companies to be in Florida and California and Arizona since at this point I assumed that solar energy was also part of the electric vehicle equation.

Electric Vehicles of America

I called Electric Vehicles of America (EVA) located in Maynard, Massachusetts. This town is relatively close to Boston; it is about a thirty minute drive west of the Route 128 beltway. The owner, Bob Batson, agreed to send me his literature in the mail, and then we would follow up with another conversation. The catalog of EVA's services seemed to show a good history of conversions, so I called Bob again. Since I already had several conversations with Solar Car Corporation, and had read about their conversion kit, I was able to ask Bob a few intelligent questions. At this point, however, I still knew very little about the equipment, time, and skills involved in converting an existing internal combustion vehicle.

As a beginner, I listened very carefully to Bob's technical advice to me about what to look for in a used pickup truck. It was very similar to what I had heard from Solar Car Corporation, and I realized that there is a "standard" for how to go about doing one of these conversions. The one big difference was that Bob advised me to plan on placing the batteries *under* the bed rather than *in* the bed, as recommended by Solar Car. This turned out to be an excellent design choice, and I will discuss the technical benefits of this battery placement later in the book.

After this initial conversation, I felt confident in Bob's ability to guide me through this conversion. I was not only impressed with his technical knowledge of how to go about conversions, but I was also encouraged by his enthusiasm and optimism about his work. He seemed to be really "into" what he was doing. He also talked about using a design and components that would provide a very safe vehicle, both in the garage and on the road. Since I was still an amateur with electricity and unsure about the dangers involved with an electric vehicle, this emphasis on safety sounded just great.

Final Selection

Based upon these phone conversations, I decided that I would go with EVA as my supplier. I was pumped up after the phone call and ready to go. If I could go back and do it over again, I would have visited Bob at his shop in Maynard before making the decision. I would certainly still have enthusiastically selected Bob's company, but I now realize that I took a chance by not seeing some of his work and visiting him in person. As you will read later, I did eventually make several trips to his shop.

Besides being encouraged by Bob's enthusiasm, I soon found out that I could trust his know-how. Bob gave me several customer contacts so I could speak with others who had converted their vehicles with Bob's help. Both of the people I talked with were very happy with Bob's service and equipment, and they were satisfied with their trucks after the conversion. Up to this point I had not heard anything that would make me change my mind on the selection of EVA.

Chapter 3

Finding a Vehicle

The Search

In June 1994 I started my search for a pickup truck to convert. I decided to convert a truck, rather than a car, for several reasons. Primarily, I decided on a truck for safety considerations. With a truck it is possible to put all of the batteries outside of the passenger compartment. I had a vision of getting into an accident and having sulfuric acid spilling out of the batteries. This may be a reason why I found truck conversions to be common as I was searching for a conversion company. It looked like many companies were doing trucks, and the conversion industry was developing a lot of experience with pickups. My wife says that the reason I picked a truck was that it is a "guy thing." I had never owned a pickup truck and here was my chance. She is probably right.

I decided to look for a Chevy S-10 or a GMC S-15. This truck seemed to be the truck of choice for conversions. I could only guess at the reasons: (1) the truck has been popular for years and is therefore widely available, and (2) the truck is also fairly light weight, and weight is such a major consideration in a conversion. All of a sudden, it seemed that everywhere I went I saw

Chevy S-10 pickups. On the road, in parking lots, and used car lots: they were everywhere. And, of course, I was interested in the newest and shiniest ones.

As I looked at these trucks, I considered Bob's advice. He suggested I look for one with a five-speed transmission, although four-speed or automatic could work. The truck should have power brakes, for good braking power since the batteries are very heavy, and manual steering, to reduce the electrical loads by eliminating the power steering pump. He told me, though, that I could later convert the steering back to manual if the original truck had power steering. I also decided that to keep the truck weight as low as possible, I would look for a regular cab with the short bed.

Frustration

The search took about three months. I visited several used car dealers in the area, and told them what I was looking for. I had decided that I did not want to spend any more than $1000 for a used truck, and hopefully less. But, unfortunately, all of the used trucks I found were in the range of $3000 to $8000. Also, the dealers were not hopeful that I could find a truck in good shape for only $1000. I knew I would never be able to afford the conversion if I spent more than $3000 on the truck. In hopes of finding someone who wanted to sell a truck for less than $3000, I put an advertisement in the classified section of the newspaper. However, after several weeks of running the ad, I did not get any phone calls.

My enthusiasm for the project helped to get me through this initial frustration. Finally, after several months of looking and advertising, I talked with a used car dealer who gave me a promising lead. First, he told me that the New York state laws concerning used car warranty discouraged the dealers from selling anything in poor shape, and therefore, I could not find one in my price range. The dealers apparently are required to provide a limited warranty which they are reluctant to do for a "clunker." This is why I could not find what I was looking for in New York. He advised me to visit another used car dealer just over the border in Pennsylvania. The laws there are different and his friend regularly picked up "clunkers" at auto auctions every week.

The Right Truck

So I drove the twenty-five miles to this dealer in Mansfield, PA on a Saturday morning. As I drove up, I immediately saw a Chevy S-10 that had promise. The truck's body was in fairly good shape, one tire was flat, and the transmission was a five-speed manual. The salesman came out to tell me all about the truck, and I liked what I heard and saw. The dealer had just purchased the truck at an auction and the six cylinder engine was "blown." Since I did not want the engine anyway, that was fine with me. The truck was a 1986 model with power steering, power brakes, regular cab, and a short bed. Just what I was hoping to find.

The salesman told me that, if I was interested, I should call the dealer on Monday to settle the details. He understood the price to be about $1500 dollars. That price seemed okay with me. I had become so frustrated with the search for a truck, I was willing to stretch my spending limit a little bit. I explained to the salesman what I was planning to do with the truck, and he seemed very intrigued and asked that I drive it back up to show it off when I was done. This was the first of many times that other people showed a lot of interest in the project.

I called the dealer on Monday to express my interest in the truck and explain what I intended to do with it. I tried to bargain with him, but he said the $1500 price was firm. Next I asked if he could have the internal combustion equipment removed before delivery. To my surprise he said that he would be happy to do that and without adding any cost to the truck. He removed the engine, the radiator, the exhaust system, and the gas tank. I am sure he got some salvage value from the parts, but this was one of the best decisions I made during the whole project. Even though I could have made back some of my money from these parts, the last thing I wanted was to have all those parts in my garage, wondering what to do with them. Also, I did not have any idea how to go about removing the parts and I probably would have spent the extra money buying the tools to do the job.

This trip to Pennsylvania was definitely one of the high points of the project. I had finally found a truck that met my needs, the price was okay, and the dealer would remove all of the "unnecessary" parts. As an added bonus he agreed to deliver the truck to me at no charge. So, at the end of September the truck was finally in my garage at home. Even though I did not have a good idea what I was doing yet, I did not think that the conversion would be more than a winter project. I was hoping to have the truck on the road when the snow cleared. These optimistic estimations came from the experts at Solar Car and EVA who claimed that the conversion should take about 100 man hours of work. That time seemed small compared to a whole winter of weekends and evenings. I guess I still had a lot to learn.

Chapter 4

Getting Started

First Steps

The conversion started slowly. There were no big physical changes in the truck for the first several months. I first ordered the electric motor and a few other parts from EVA. While waiting for that order, the initial stage of the project seemed to mostly involve taking things apart rather than putting things together. I spent several hours finding and removing parts of the truck that were no longer needed. Things like the radiator overflow tank, catalytic converter heat shield, and other small parts. This helped to lighten the truck, but if I did not know what it was, I left it. While much of this was fun, the truck also needed quite a bit of cleanup inside and out. Given that the truck also had over 112,000 miles on the odometer, it was sure to need a lot of automotive repair in addition to all of the conversion work. (On the bright side, I made about fifty cents by returning the empty cans and bottles from the bed.) Since I did not know the logical steps to follow in the conversion, I took Bob's advice to start on the clutch and transmission.

I sent the clutch pressure plate to Bob, as he requested, so he could do some modifications. He had to describe to me what it looked like since I had already exhausted my automotive knowledge. Luckily the used car dealer had sent along a box of miscellaneous parts left over from the engine removal. This clutch pressure plate was in the box even though I did not know to ask for it to be included. The clutch pressure plate would be used to help couple the electric motor shaft to the transmission shaft. For a good in-depth discussion of the motor to transmission mounting, see Brant (1994, pp. 268-272).

The clutch itself, however, does not perform a traditional function in this design. The clutch does not disconnect the motor from the transmission – the motor is always connected to the transmission. Disconnecting the motor from the rest of the drive train, while the accelerator is pushed, could cause the motor to over speed and fail. I was able to spend some time removing components associated with the clutch system. I left the clutch pedal in, however, so that my son, Michael, then nine years old, could sit in the truck and pretend to drive and shift.

Transmission

The next step was to remove the transmission. The shaft of the transmission required some machining at the local transmission shop, to help with the motor-to-transmission mounting. Bob gave me complete instructions over the phone about how much of the shaft to remove. Since I could not drive the truck to the shop, I decided to try to remove the transmission and take it in myself. While this may seem like a simple endeavor for someone with experience, it was not so easy for me. Before I got started, I went to the bookstore to find a repair guide for the Chevy S-10. The Chilton's book that I bought turned out to be valuable throughout the whole conversion since it showed me how to remove and re-install a lot of different parts, including the transmission.

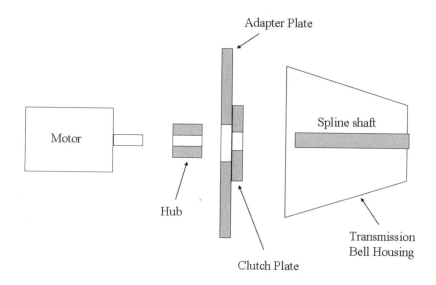

FIGURE 1. Motor to transmission mounting.

It took me about two weeks of evening work to remove the transmission. Freeing the bolts holding the transmission to the frame was the biggest problem, because of all the road dirt and rust on the bolts. At this time I purchased a hydraulic floor jack and jack stands to give me more room under the truck, since I was spending a lot of time down there on my back. Those tools proved to be invaluable during the whole conversion. A can of WD-40 also helped a lot to break through the rust.

After removing the mounting bolts, I next had to remove the drive shaft which connects the transmission to the rear axle. This was relatively easy compared to the transmission bolts. I thought I was then ready to drop the transmission to the floor. As I dropped it, however, I discovered that the parking brake cable was still in the way. So after disconnecting this cable, the transmission was finally dropped off the truck. I did get a lot of transmission oil on the floor, through the hole left by the drive shaft – another opportunity to learn from my mistakes.

The Electric Motor

The actual machining work on the transmission turned out to be fairly routine and inexpensive and I had it back in a few days. Meanwhile, the electric motor had arrived from EVA. This twenty-eight horsepower DC electric motor is manufactured by Advanced DC Motors of Syracuse, New York. The motor is very small but very heavy. It is about sixteen inches long and nine inches in diameter. The motor did not appear big enough to power the truck. While I was surprised by the motor's small size, I was more surprised by the weight; it weighs about 160 pounds. Luckily, the truck driver who delivered the motor was a strong guy because I could not move it myself. This is why the motor remained on the garage floor for the next six months while all of the prep work was done.

Along with the motor, Bob also sent his conversion manual and wiring diagrams. The manual was a very complete description of the conversion steps. It really helped to be able to read ahead and to see the whole conversion process. I found that Bob was very open with this process and very helpful over the phone, as I was now calling him weekly with lots of questions. After the first month of the project, I was satisfied that I had made the right decision in choosing EVA to support me.

**FIGURE 2. A top view of the motor, shown installed at the end of the
project.**

Steering

The next project was the steering. Bob recommended that I convert the steering from power to manual to eliminate the power steering pump as a drain on the batteries. The Chilton manual called for a special tool, a pitman arm removal tool, to disconnect the gear from the steering system. So I went to the tool rental shop to rent it, and I had to guess which of two different size tools might work.

As it turned out, the pitman arm removal tool that I selected did not work. It was too small to fit over the pitman arm. So I returned to the tool rental shop for the other one. When I tried that one, it proved to be too large; it would slip whenever I tried to separate the pitman joint. The rental shop manager said that those were the only two standard sizes available. I knew I did not want to go the GM dealer to buy this tool because I would probably never use it again. I considered using force – that is, using a hammer to pound the joint apart. The rental shop manager did not recommend this as there was a good chance of causing severe damage to the steering system. So I decided to leave that project and hopefully find someone later who could help.

In the meantime I managed to find a manual steering gear to put into the truck. Compared to the dilemma above, it was relatively easy. I contacted an auto salvage yard, and they indicated that they had one still installed on an S-10 wreck. They needed a day to get it off and then I could pick it up. Driving there the next day was an adventure. The salvage yard was about forty miles away and on a remote dirt road. It was a rainy day and the road was very muddy – a challenge for my little Geo Metro. But the gear was ready as promised and cost about $80. I had no idea if that was a good price and I did not know if the gear would work when installed. Oh well – I was just happy to be making some kind of progress.

Adapter Plate

The last project in this early part of the conversion process was to prepare the adapter plate. This large ½ inch thick aluminum plate is used to mount the motor, clutch pressure plate, and transmission together. The outside rim of the adapter plate mounts to the transmission bell housing. Bob sent my adapter plate as a large square, about twenty inches on each side, with a hole in the center. The adapter plate then had to be machined and drilled to match my transmission shape and hole pattern. A good description of the adapter plate can be found in Prange (1993, pp. 40-42).

The most sensitive part of the alignment plate work is to make sure the hole in the center of the alignment plate is centered around the transmission shaft. All of these drive components must align fairly well for the motor to work efficiently. Bob sent an alignment tool to make this alignment almost foolproof. One end of the tool fits over the transmission shaft while the other end fits into the hole in the center of the adapter plate.

Preparing the plate for machining by myself was difficult. I stood up the transmission on its small end (a real balancing act), placed the adapter plate on top, and inserted the alignment tool. I then clamped the plate and transmission together with three small C-clamps to maintain the aligned position. Next I flipped everything over so that the adapter plate was flat on the garage floor. In this position, I traced the transmission bell housing holes on the plate as a guide for the machine shop. Also, I marked where a considerable amount of the plate could be trimmed off, since the plate was a square, much larger than the outside of the transmission bell housing.

The machine shop made quick work of the adapter plate. The machinist drilled the holes and trimmed off the excess and had it back in a few days. The machinist just happened to have a bell housing similar to mine in his shop so he was able to verify the hole pattern. Unfortunately he could not also check the alignment of the center hole in the plate. When Bob sent me the alignment tool, he told me a story about a catastrophic failure of an electric truck because of a poor alignment between the motor and transmission. So until the truck actually worked okay, I would have this nagging concern about whether I had done this step properly.

I planned at this point to re-install the transmission and install the motor. I knew I would need help and special tools for this heavy work. I figured an engine hoist would be able to lift the motor into place. I procrastinated so long, however, that instead of doing this work myself, I found someone who really knew what he was doing.

FIGURE 3. The adapter plate installed. In the foreground is the motor.
The bolts on the outside edge of the adapter plate connect to the
transmission bell housing.

Chapter 5

Fabrication and Welding

Battery Location

The next step, while I tried to figure out the motor installation, was to install the battery box steel supports. Bob's design called for the installation of sixteen batteries under the truck's bed and four batteries up front where the radiator was removed. The four batteries up front help to balance the weight distribution of the truck so that the truck has a level attitude. One of the biggest reasons he offered for the location of the rear sixteen batteries was that this placement lowered the center of gravity of the vehicle and thus provided better handling on the road. Some designs, such as Solar Car, place the rear batteries inside the bed. Another benefit of Bob's design is that the bed is still available for hauling (although the weight capacity would diminish due to the 1500 pounds of batteries the truck would be carrying). Additionally, the under-bed installation is safer since the batteries are below the driver and passenger level. In case of an accident, the rear batteries would not be able to penetrate the cab.

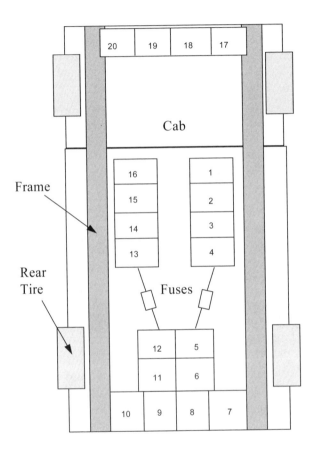

FIGURE 1. The location of the batteries, including the front battery box with four batteries and the three rear battery boxes with a total of sixteen.

Steel Fabrication

All of these batteries fit inside polyethylene boxes (one box can hold up to eight batteries). These battery boxes need support and protection. Bob provided drawings of the structural steel required for the battery box supports. I then tried to find a shop that would do both the fabrication of the steel and the welding. I first tried a small fabrication shop only about a mile from home. I had a vision of towing the truck to their shop for the installation. It almost seemed too easy. They showed a lot of interest but thought it was too small of a project for them.

My next stop was a very large fabrication company much farther away. Despite their size, the manager was interested and accepted the fabricating job at a very reasonable price. His shop would not do the installation, but he recommended a local welder who could do a very good job on the truck. I provided him with the drawings of the steel, provided by Bob, and he gave me a grand tour of their large facility and their current projects. I felt confident they would do a good job.

In order to do the job properly, the manager wanted to make sure they used the correct gauge (thickness) of bar stock in fabricating the battery box steel. The drawings were not clear, so we called Bob to make sure. He said we certainly had a choice, but to be sure we erred on the safe side. As someone who had never operated an electric vehicle, I did not consider overall vehicle weight at this point. We selected 3/16 inch thick bar stock for the steel supports, since it was a standard size and appeared to be rather strong. In hindsight, I wonder if I could have saved considerable weight with smaller gauge steel, and still had a safe vehicle.

FIGURE 4. One of the rear battery boxes that holds four batteries, with one inch thick styrofoam insulation on the sides.

Several weeks later I picked up the completed steel parts with my little Geo. The steel easily fit in back of the car, but it was very heavy. The car looked comical going down the highway with the front end riding high and the back end riding low. While the car looked funny, I got very tired loading and unloading the very heavy steel.

Welding the Steel

While I was waiting for the fabrication to be completed, I contacted the welder to see if he was interested in the job. His name is Kevin Gardner of Gardner's Welding, a one man business. On the phone he sounded very interested and asked to see the truck. When Kevin got a look at the truck and the steel, he seemed excited about getting involved in the project. Because of his interest in the project, Kevin quoted me a price below his normal hourly rate, which I was pleased to accept. I had always assumed that a welder would bring his equipment to the truck, and do the job at my garage. Rather than doing the job in my garage with mobile equipment, he suggested towing the truck to his shop, about thirty miles away. Kevin felt he could do a better job at his place with all of his equipment, tools, and a familiar surrounding.

It turned out that Kevin lives close to a major racetrack in Watkins Glen, New York. He has quite a bit of experience repairing race cars during the race season. Knowing this helped a lot with my confidence in getting a good result. His automotive experience proved to be valuable, as he also suggested some other work that would end up making this whole project much easier for me in the long run. First, he suggested sandblasting and painting the frame of the truck. The frame was pretty rusty, but the body was in reasonable shape. This would end up giving the truck a much better look. The new steel work would also blend in much better with a newly finished frame. He recommended a friend nearby who could do the sandblasting at a very reasonable price, and I accepted.

27

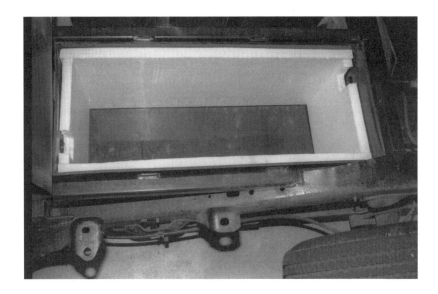

FIGURE 5. Top photo: The support steel for one of the rear battery boxes. Bottom photo: The polyethylene box in place.

Major Automotive Work

Additionally, Kevin volunteered to install the motor, transmission, and other parts of the drive train. Since I was not looking forward to this task, I agreed to this work as well. He arrived a few days later to pick up the truck and all of the parts. He borrowed a flat bed tow truck for this job, which saved me a lot of money and coordination. Also, all the other truck and steel parts fit easily into the back of his pickup truck. The "gutted" truck was easily maneuverable at this point. Without the engine, motor, transmission, and other internal combustion engine parts, two people could easily push it over to the tow truck.

At this point in early March, only five months since I had bought the truck, I felt like I was making good progress. I still believed (naively) that I could finish the conversion by the end of spring. Kevin's part of the project, however, ended up taking much longer than I had anticipated. He had a lot of other projects going on at the time, and he was doing a lot for me. As far as automotive work on the truck, my work list for Kevin was growing. I still had not successfully converted the steering to manual, so he agreed to install the manual steering gear. He also replaced the parking brake cables which were badly rusted. After the conversion was completed, I was extremely grateful for this because I would find that the parking brake (or a curb) was about all that would stop the truck from rolling away. Without the engine compression to hold the truck in place, it will roll on even the slightest incline.

I visited the truck once a month for the three months that Kevin had it in his shop. I marveled at the changes. He really did a wonderful job in converting the truck. What I saw really gave me confidence that the whole design would come together successfully. I learned that I could do this project without automotive experience of my own: just hire someone who knows what he is doing.

Unfortunately, because this was my first time doing a conversion, I cut corners on a key improvement at this point and ended up paying for it later. Bob had repeatedly told me to be sure to add strength to the rear suspension. The batteries weigh about seventy pounds each, so with sixteen batteries in the rear, the truck was carrying about 1,100 pounds, with nothing in the bed! An effective way to address this problem is to add an extra set of leaf springs to the rear. I could have bought a set for Kevin to install but instead we decided to bolt on a set of "helper" springs. These less expensive springs (about $40) attach to the existing springs to give the suspension more capacity. At this point, without the batteries installed yet, I could not tell if this solution would work. It did not work well, but I was still months from knowing that.

Tilt Bed

In addition to installing the steel battery box supports, he also converted the bed to a hinged tilt bed, to provide access to the sixteen rear batteries. This was a key part of Bob's overall truck design. After removing the bolts which hold the bed in place, Kevin welded hinges to the rear edge of the frame and bed. He also welded two threaded studs to the underside of the bed so that I could use wing nuts to lock down the bed. Otherwise the bed could fly up or vibrate while driving. Lastly, he welded on two more studs to the underside of the bed and the frame so that I could brace the bed in the raised position for maintenance. I use a length of PVC pipe for the brace – it is lightweight and easily stowed behind the driver's seat.

Another aspect of Kevin's work was to provide support for the control board, which I will discuss in the next chapter. And, lastly, he installed a "torque rod." This metal bar anchors the transmission to the truck body. Its purpose is to counter the torque generated by the rotation of the motor and transmission, thereby reducing twisting stress on the motor mounts and

FIGURE 6. The bed is shown in the up position with the PVC pipe holding it in place.

transmission mounts. Kevin used rubber mounts in attaching the torque rod, to smooth out any vibrations transmitted to the truck body from the motor and transmission.

In May, Kevin brought back the truck. He had transformed the truck from an internal combustion engine vehicle to one ready for wiring and batteries. The steel battery box supports were painted black to match the refinished frame. This steel looked like it had always been a part of the truck. The motor, transmission, adapter plate, clutch plate, and drive shaft were all installed and ready to run (and hopefully aligned properly). With all of the automotive work that he did, I was ready to concentrate on the wiring and batteries. This was no longer a winter project, but surely the end was in sight.

Chapter 6

Control Wiring

Control Board

In April, I started to work on the twelve volt control circuits. The converted truck retains most of its original twelve volt circuits including a standard twelve volt battery. This twelve volt system is then used to control the operation of the new electric drive system, as well as to supply loads such as lights, horn, wipers, etc. First I set out to make the control board. This board, which is located just under the hood, holds all of the components and wiring for the control circuits. Bob designed this board so the owner would have one central location for all of the control system, to make maintenance and troubleshooting easier.

The control board is made out of MDO board. I am not sure what the initials stand for. This is a type of strong plywood with a very smooth surface. I had a pattern from Bob, but very few carpentry tools and skills. Luckily, my boss at work, Ev Larson, is a furniture maker. He was very excited about this project and gladly agreed to help me shape this control board. I knew I would get an excellent product because I had seen his furniture. The job took us about four hours. We started with the MDO board (30 x 40 inches) supplied by Bob. The shaping involved cutting the outside contour and also drilling holes for the high voltage welding cables, which connect the motor and batteries with the control system components. Also, one very large rectangular hole was cut to help cool the controller because it is the largest and heaviest component on the control board and it can get very hot during operation.

A Quality Paint Job

My son Michael now had a chance to get into the act. He was always looking for opportunities to contribute to the project; so I let him spray paint the control board. Painting for ten year-old kids is great fun, but his Mom was concerned about where else the paint might go. I kept her inside during this step so she could not see what was going on! When Michael recruited his friend Laura to help, I became concerned as I remembered another painting incident when Michael and Laura were six years old. One summer I was painting the garage door and they wanted to help. Not wanting a mess on the garage and its windows, I set them up in the driveway with some pieces of scrap wood, some old brushes, and their own can of paint. This arrangement was going pretty well until a neighbor stopped by to chat. While I was distracted with my back turned, the kids showed their age. When I turned to look at them, they had painted the bottoms of their feet and were making white footprints on the driveway. Luckily they were using latex paint, which hosed off the concrete rather easily.

The children revealed how they had matured in four years, and this painting job went very well. Soon, they had applied a gray primer coat and a royal blue finish coat which somewhat matched the truck's blue body color. After the paint dried, I took the control board to Kevin's shop. At this time, he was still working on the battery box support steel and the tilt bed hinges.

I had also asked him to mount the control board in the engine compartment. The board sits in the engine compartment, above

FIGURE 8. Top photo: The finished control board installed at the end of the conversion. Bottom photo: The board in the up position for access to the motor and front batteries.

the motor and four of the batteries. The board holds the major electrical components (other than the motor and batteries) in one place. Square aluminum tubes that reach up from the motor mounts support the board at its rear edge. Kevin's design for the board support was very creative and works extremely well. His design mounts these square tubes on the motor mounts rather than the adapter plate as used in some designs. His design, I believe, results in a simple and strong support.

The board is hinged in the rear so that the board can lift up, providing access to the motor and front four batteries. At the front, the control board is screwed down, using wing nuts, to the front battery box structure. This prevents the board from moving around during operation. I delivered the control board to Kevin so that he could install the hinge brackets to the board and complete the mounting design.

Control Board Components

After Kevin completed fitting up the control board, I brought it back home to start mounting components and wiring the control circuits. Mounting the components proved to be the easy part. Bob had provided a drawing of the board and the mounting locations. All I needed was a drill and some hardware. After taking some measurements, I made what would be my first of over twenty trips to a hardware store for nuts, bolts, washers, and lock washers. If I had known this earlier, I would have bought a large quantity of these items, to save me trips back and forth to the store. I rarely had more than two hours at a time to spend on the truck, so I was always buying just enough hardware to accomplish a meaningful task. Each of these little "meaningful" tasks seemed to require something just a little bit different in terms of hardware. As a result, none of the hardware is standardized, but it works and the truck has character.

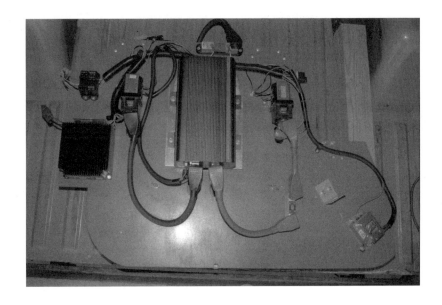

FIGURE 9. Photo: A top view of the control board, with all of the components and wiring installed, before going into the engine compartment.

The board was very heavy with all of the components mounted. The controller, DC to DC converter, and contactors all added weight. I could still lift the board to move it, but it was a challenge. I also needed to mount a fan underneath the board to help cool the controller. Because the fan is the only component which mounts underneath the board, moving the board around then became an effort to not damage this fan accidentally.

Control Wiring

Up until this point, I was pretty confident that I knew what I was doing. I understood the general concept of the truck's electric motor and batteries. The batteries would supply energy to the motor. Occasionally the batteries would require charging. I quickly found out, however, how little I knew about the control circuits, and why they were necessary. I also discovered that I did not know very much about electrical wiring.

I now had a control board with the control components mounted. It looked great. I also had the wiring diagram for the control circuits and the power circuit (the power circuit is a whole story in itself). I also had a lot of color-coded wires that Bob had sent along with the components. I sat on the floor of my family room with all of these parts and stared at them. I studied the wiring diagram over and over. I finally realized that I did not have a clue where to start. I had no idea what to do first. This was a very humbling moment. The wiring diagram was very foreign to me. I was not able to picture what all of the lines on paper would look like as real wires on the control board.

Looking back on it now, I understand why I did not know what to do. I had never done any wiring, either automotive or house-hold. I had done nothing more than replacing a plug on the end of a lamp cord or installing a new light bulb socket in a lamp. I certainly did not understand twelve volt DC automotive wiring and had never done it. So I again called Bob to get his help.

FIGURE 10. This is the controller which directs power from the batteries to the motor, based on a signal from the potbox. The controller gets very hot during operation and is cooled by a fan under the control board.

FIGURE 11. One of the contactors that open and shut the circuit between the motor, batteries, and controller. The primary contactor shuts when the ignition key is turned on. The secondary contactor shuts when the potbox is activated by the accelerator.

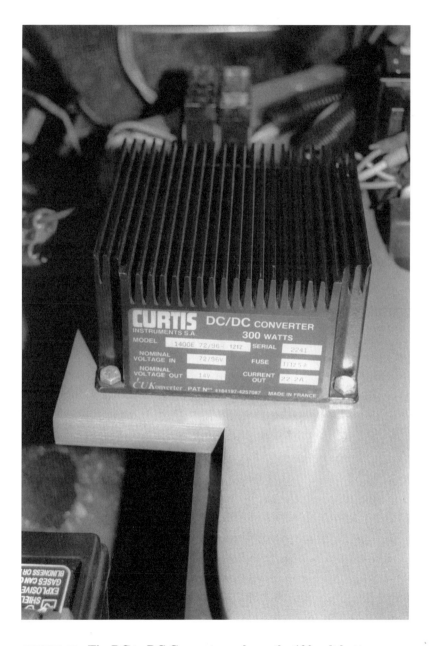

FIGURE 12. The DC to DC Converter reduces the 120 volt battery
voltage to 15 volts and uses this lower voltage to keep the twelve volt
battery charged.

However, there was little he could do for me over the phone. I could not afford a huge phone bill nor could I afford to fly him to my home in New York. He tried to describe to me what to do and I tried out his instructions, but I still was unable to get started. After several weeks of no progress I got lucky. I had to go on a business trip to Waltham, Massachusetts in late July. Waltham is only a thirty minute drive from Bob's business in Maynard. I called him to see if I could stop by on my way back home to get some coaching. He was very open to this idea, since he wants all of his customers to get their vehicles on the road and to be satisfied with the results. I was not happy with the further delay, but I was glad to be getting some help.

Road Trip to Bob's Shop

Even though it would take seven hours, I decided to drive to Waltham rather than fly. Driving allowed me to bring my control board and wiring to Bob's shop. We planned to work together for a whole day, but I was not sure how much we could accomplish. I also packed a camera, hoping to take some photos of Bob's truck. At that time he drove a Chevy S-10 pickup truck that he had converted several years before. This was his demonstration truck, and it was a beautiful vehicle.

I arrived at his business, Electric Vehicles of America, at 9:00 AM. Bob was already in the shop working on a vehicle. Because he and his wife are the only employees and they have worked very hard to build the business from scratch, he normally gets to work very early and stays late. Bob stopped what he was doing and gave me a very warm greeting. Then we immediately started to set up my control board in a corner of the shop.

Bob appeared to be having a very busy day, even without training me. He was replacing the batteries in a Saturn sedan that day. This vehicle was owned and operated by a local utility.

Bob worked on that vehicle in between coaching me and keeping me on track. In addition, he took numerous phone calls and talked with visitors to the shop.

Learning Wiring

After our phone conversations, Bob knew he had to start training me with the basics. He first showed me how the control wires were color coded for identification and how the codes matched the wiring diagram. Then he showed me how to set up the fuse box which is the starting point for all wires entering and leaving the control board. Once that was set I started to make progress. He also showed me how to use several different types of crimping tools that I had never seen before. I learned fast because after he showed me what to do, he had me do the actual work. Because of Bob's teaching style, I was more able to do the work myself when I returned home.

By noon, I had managed to mount the fuse box, wire the fuse box, and start to connect some of the wires to the control board components. I was slowly coming to see how the wiring diagram translated into real wiring. When I tried to interpret the wiring diagram literally, I realized I would end up connecting wires in illogical places, or places where connections do not exist. As I had viewed it before Bob's instructions, the wiring diagram sometimes looked like it called for splicing wires out in the middle of nowhere. After Bob's explanation, I could suddenly see things coming together. He showed me that if you can envision where the electricity is flowing, you can decide the best location to connect a wire. It was a relatively simple solution to my earlier confusion.

We stopped for lunch in early afternoon. The day had turned out to be very hot and humid – in the mid 90's. Bob's wife Donna brought in lunch for us from a local restaurant and we ate in their lunchroom which adjoins the office and the shop. We talked about how and why Bob had started the business in the early

1990's. It all started when he converted a vehicle to electric power in the late 1980's. After deciding to leave his corporate engineering job of twenty-five years, he started his own company to do conversions and sell components to others like myself who wanted to do their own conversions. I am very impressed at how Bob has established himself in the electric vehicle industry in such a short period of time.

After lunch I continued to work on the board until about 6:00 PM. I made a lot of progress, but I would return home with the control board wiring only about thirty percent complete. I finished up the day by taking a close look at Bob's truck and taking photographs of the details for later reference at home. As it turned out, those photographs saved me a lot of time and prevented many mistakes which could have resulted from guessing at the proper wire installation. The photographs later gave me much needed confidence in Bob's absence.

Test Drive

Before I left to drive home, Bob suggested that we take his truck out for a spin. I jumped at the chance, since I had only driven an electric once, when I first visited his shop briefly in November 1994. We took the truck out for a short drive around the neighborhood. The truck drove very smoothly and, as you might guess, was fairly quiet except for the road noise.

Driving the electric truck is considerably different from driving a comparable gas powered truck. The truck rides smoothly and quietly, and you do not feel the gasoline engine's vibration and power. On the down side, the truck is less responsive from a standing start and during acceleration. Switching from gas to electric is like switching from a Pentium computer back to a 386 computer. You can still do what you want to do, but you must have more patience with your vehicle. An exception to this may be the new General Motors EV1 which, according to reviews, is every bit as quick as most gasoline powered cars.

The drive in Bob's truck helped to inspire me to get home and finish up the wiring and the rest of my truck. I could not wait to get my own vehicle on the road. The skills and knowledge I learned from Bob would carry me through the next two months of work on the wiring. The wiring job, however, would turn out to be much more difficult at home.

Continuing the Job at Home

I set up for the wiring job in my garage with the board on the lowered tailgate. I soon discovered how easy it had been in Bob's shop. All of the proper tools, wire, and connectors were instantly available in his shop. And most importantly, Bob was there for training and feedback. I had none of these at home; instead I had the color-coded wire, the wiring diagram, and the photos of Bob's truck.

Over the next two months, working in two-hour blocks of time, I was able to complete the wiring on the board. This included numerous trips to the auto parts store for various connectors of the right shape and gauge. As with the nuts and bolts hardware, I went to the store for only what I needed at the moment. The store clerks certainly got to know me very well! I learned that I probably could have saved time by just buying an assorted box of connectors.

As I mentioned before, one of the biggest problems I had during this wiring project was interpreting the wiring diagram and turning it into reality. When you look at completed wiring it does not necessarily "look" like the wiring diagram. As Bob taught me, you have to think in terms of how the electricity will flow to figure out where to connect the end of a wire. Additionally, a length of wire may end up being twice as long as it appears on a diagram. The best place for a wire is not necessarily the shortest path from point A to point B. A wire may need to go around components and stay in a "wiring run" to give a neat appearance and not get in the way during maintenance.

Safe and Neat Wiring

Bob also taught me several tricks for producing neat, orderly, and safe control wiring. One method is to use a material called "heat shrink tubing" to give the wire and connectors a finished look and safe operation. This shrink tubing fits over the gap where the wire and connector come together. Without this tubing, there may be a gap with exposed copper wiring. After fitting a piece of the tubing over this gap, a heat gun is used to shrink the tubing to a tight fit which permanently covers the exposed wire. The result is also a professional looking connection which helps to give the whole control board a finished look. I rented a heat gun from the local tool rental store about five times during the conversion project. I probably paid as much for these rentals as it would have cost to buy a new heat gun.

Another trick to produce a neat control board is to use "split loom", which is a black plastic tubing with a lengthwise split. The split allows wires to be easily inserted into the loom but does not allow the wires to easily fall out. The loom comes in different sizes from an auto parts store. Placing wires inside the loom gives a neat an orderly appearance, but it does more. The loom also prevents wires from tangling or interfering with control board components such as the contactors or pot box which have moving parts. Additionally, the loom prevents wires from chaffing or being accidentally pulled during routine maintenance. I liked the loom idea so much that I also used it for other systems that I installed later, such as the vacuum system, the charging system, and the heater.

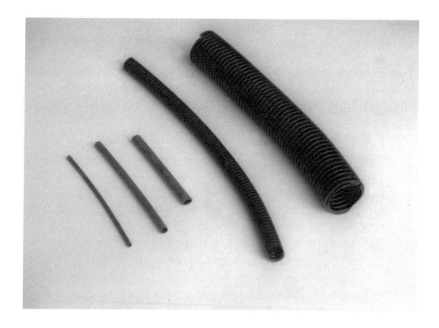

FIGURE 13. Top photo: Shows the different sizes of heat shrink tubing and split loom. Bottom Photo: Shows an example of finished wiring with the heat shrink tubing and split loom installed.

Voltage and Current Gages

The last parts of the control wiring installation were the gages to monitor voltage and current. These gages are a key part of the control wiring when driving the truck. The voltmeter displays the total voltage of the battery pack, and the ammeter shows how much current is being drawn out of the batteries when the accelerator is pushed.

The voltmeter functions like a fuel gage in a car – it shows how much energy you have left in the battery pack. You must know, however, how much voltage corresponds to "empty". This mostly comes from experience or from having someone like Bob who can give you an idea how to use this gage. "Fuel" gages are made for electric vehicles, but due to the cost, I decided to wait until later to install one. A fuel gage indicates how much of the total charge is left, just like a car's fuel gage. The voltmeter and ammeter were about $50 each, but the fuel gage costs about $250. I have an empty spot on the gage panel waiting for the fuel gage. Meanwhile, I use the voltmeter to tell me when it is time to get home for a charge.

The ammeter shows how much current, or amps, are flowing out of the battery pack to the motor. This gage is invaluable if you are trying to drive conservatively to maximize the vehicle's range. It would be the same as having a "miles per gallon" meter in your car.

The installation of the gages requires a number of wires to go from the control board in the engine compartment to the gages on the dashboard. My first strategy was to use an existing hole in the fire wall, one used by other wires under the glove compartment. The main wire bundle in this area, however, was so tightly packed with wires that I could not even push one small wire through to the other side.

The second candidate hole was the one used by the radio antenna wire. All six wires pushed through this hole very easily. This

FIGURE 14. The ammeter and voltmeter installed just below the radio.

solution seemed too easy. When I told Bob what I had done, he cautioned against this since the new wires could interfere with the radio reception. So the last resort was to drill a new hole through the fire wall in this same area. When I finally got the nerve to do this, it turned out fine. The hole drilled easily and then I installed a rubber grommet to protect the wires from chaffing on the edges of the hole (I found the proper size grommet easily at the local hardware store).

I had to decide where to mount the gages on the dashboard. The only good place I found was at the ashtray, below the radio. Since I do not smoke, removing the ashtray was not a problem. I bought a gage panel from the NAPA store, with room for three gages, in anticipation of eventually putting in a fuel gage.

After all the experience I had gained with the other control wiring, the wiring of the gages was not difficult (the wiring instructions were included on Bob's wiring diagram). The gages also come with small lights so that the dials are visible during night driving. These lights must be wired separately from the gages into the twelve volt system. This was very delicate work since the lighting wires are very, very small. This also resulted in two more wires through the fire wall.

Bob told me that it is easy to wire these gages backwards at this point. It is not dangerous, but on starting up the truck, a back-wards wired gage would read zero instead of the correct voltage or amperage. (As luck would have it, I did not need to rewire the gages after starting up the truck. I guessed right.)

Power to the Control Board

At this point all of the components were on the board and wired together. Yet, I still was not entirely confident that I had done it right. I really wanted to buy an airline ticket for Bob and have him inspect my work in my garage! Instead, I settled for a lot of phone calls. I probably talked with him once a week during this wiring work. I especially needed his help during this next phase – connecting the control board to a power source.

Twelve volt power from the truck must come onto the board to operate the main contactors, run the cooling fan, and provide power for other components. However, I did not know where to get this twelve volt power. Along the fire wall I could see literally dozens of exposed wires left over from the removal of the internal combustion engine. It looked like spaghetti to me. Somewhere in there was a power wire from the ignition switch. I had skimped on cost by not buying a wiring diagram book for the Chevy S-10 and now I was paying for it. (Note: I still have not bought one.)

Bob coached me through this one on the phone, and when I still did not "get it" he sent me a fax with a drawing of the junction box on the fire wall which would eventually hold the wires going into and out of the ignition switch. First, he told me to get a multimeter with the continuity function. I went down to Radio Shack and bought an inexpensive meter, which turned out to be one of the best and most useful tools I have for the truck. It is a little pocket-sized, battery-powered multimeter that can fit into tight places and stores easily. It also works great to check if the house water heater elements are burned out.

Success!

Next, Bob told me to look into the "spaghetti" for two red or pink wires of the heavier ten to twelve gauge size. When I found them I could check for continuity of these wires since they both run to the ignition switch. One is always "hot" from the battery, and the other is energized when the ignition switch is on. Sure enough, I did find two wires of that description. I hooked up the multimeter probes to the ends of these wires and checked the continuity with the ignition switch on (at this point I did not yet have a twelve volt battery in the truck, so there was not actually any twelve volt power). Miraculously, the continuity was positive (indicating a complete circuit), and when I turned off the ignition switch, the circuit was broken. I have to admit that this was one of the most exciting moments of my conversion experience. I actually found something that worked! It was also a key step if I wanted to make *any* more progress on this truck.

As far as the rest of the spaghetti is concerned, it is still there, pushed out of the way. In one sense, it is a little reminder of what the truck used to be. In reality, I am so uncertain of what is in there that I do not want to mess with it any more than necessary. As I would find out months later, some important wires still lurked in there.

Rejuvenation

In August as I was working on the control wiring, my parents sent me a book on electric vehicles for my birthday. The book, by Noel Perrin, was a joy to read and gave me renewed energy to push ahead to complete the conversion. Perrin recounted his experience in trying to drive an electric Ford Escort from California back to his home in New England. His resourcefulness in making the electric car work in a gasoline world was very encouraging. If he could travel that far in the Escort (he did not make it all the way), I could surely use the truck successfully as a local commuter vehicle.

Adding Twelve Volt Power

After wiring up the ignition wire to the control board, I bought a twelve volt battery for the truck. The design of this vehicle calls for the twelve volt system to remain intact. All of the truck's accessories continue to use twelve volt power from a standard automotive battery. This simplifies the conversion, but also provides a safety feature. As Bob explains it, if you get stranded on the highway due to a main battery problem, this battery is still

FIGURE 15. The junction box on the fire wall that connects to the ignition switch.

there to provide power to your hazard warning lights (and cellular phone) until you can get some help.

I bought the smallest and least expensive battery I could find. I figured that this battery would not be called on to start the internal combustion engine in cold weather. It was only there to provide standard twelve volt services and to close the contactors on the control board. A small one would do just fine.

After installing the battery, I was itching to see if everything worked. Up to this point, the truck had just been a dead hulk. I had never seen the wipers, radio, fan, lights, or anything else work. So one day after work, I hooked up the battery, sat in the driver's seat, and turned on the ignition. I almost jumped through the roof in fright. Not only did everything work, but everything was on "full blast" when I turned on the ignition. I immediately turned off the ignition and took some deep breaths to relax. I instantly knew what had happened. My son's favorite past time was to sit in the truck and pretend he was a delivery truck or bus driver. The last time he was "driving," he left the wipers, radio, and fan on full, and I had not bothered to check them first. I also had to pick up all of my wiring diagrams which went flying when the wipers moved. I had been using the wipers and the windshield as my desk in the garage.

Chapter 7

Vacuum System for the Power Brakes

With all of the control wiring done, I turned my attention to the brakes. Bob recommended that I keep the power brake option on the truck. The truck becomes so heavy with the added battery weight that you need all of the stopping power you can get. Power brakes apparently require a vacuum, but the vacuum must come from somewhere. With the internal combustion engine and its associated systems removed, I would have to install a vacuum system. Bob's solution is to install a vacuum pump to provide a vacuum to the power brake booster, along with a vacuum switch to turn the pump on and off as needed. Since I knew as little about brakes as I did about wiring, I could tell this would be another learning experience.

Bob provided all of the components and the wiring diagrams to accomplish the task. His instructions and diagrams proved to be accurate and helpful, as usual. My big problem was where to mount the vacuum pump and switch. The control board takes up a lot of room, the twelve volt battery takes up space, and four of the six-volt batteries are mounted where the radiator was located in the truck's previous life.

That only leaves the area around the wheel well on the driver's side. The vacuum switch mounted easily on the inside of the fender, using existing bolt holes from some previously removed parts. It was a tight squeeze, however, to get the vacuum pump to fit on top of the wheel well. It finally went in between the control board and the vacuum switch. The main problem was how to mount the pump on the wheel well, because, as Bob told me, the vacuum pump vibrates significantly during operation and the vibrations could affect the whole truck body. Some type of insulation was needed. I called an electrical supply store to see if they carried any rubber shock mounts used for pumps and motors. The store had rubber mounts with ¼ inch studs and these worked out very well.

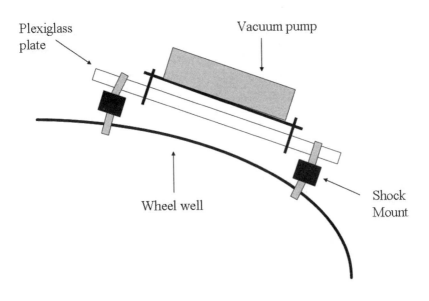

FIGURE 16. The mounting design for the vacuum pump.

FIGURE 17. The vacuum pump on the left and the vacuum switch on the right.

The other problem was how to mount the flat-bottomed pump to the very curved wheel well. Luckily, the rubber mounts are flexible enough to account for that curvature. Another problem was that the mounting holes in the pump casing were too small for the rubber mount studs. I solved that by getting a piece of ¼ inch thick Plexiglas (lightweight and strong) to hold the pump. The Plexiglas was then bolted to the wheel well using the rubber mounts.

I was concerned about drilling holes through the Plexiglas, but the glass store employee suggested that I should heat up the drill bit before drilling so that the bit would both drill and melt to prevent cracking. This method worked very well. The last step was to mount the pump to the Plexiglas and then the Plexiglas to the wheel well.

The vacuum pump and switch also needed to be wired to each other and to the twelve volt power. Bob provided a very detailed wiring diagram, and with all of my new wiring skills and experience, the wiring did not take long. Lastly, I needed to connect the pump and switch to the power brake booster with vacuum hose. This also went well with an accurate diagram to follow. Bob continued to provide me with excellent diagrams and instructions – he could not take anything for granted with my skills and experience.

Relocation to Pennsylvania

I wanted to make sure the brakes were working well because I was planning to move from New York to central Pennsylvania, to a very hilly area. Before the move I had the truck towed to a local repair shop to have the brakes checked. Since the next step in the conversion was to add the batteries, the truck would become very heavy and therefore be difficult to stop. The repair shop fixed a brake line leak and replaced some brake pads. This gave me a lot more confidence that the truck was really ready for the batteries, which I intended to install after the move to

Pennsylvania. The repair shop also opened up the differential and replaced the lubricant with a lightweight oil. Bob had recommend-ed this light lubrication as one of the ways to reduce the drive train friction and therefore help extend the truck's range on a battery charge.

The truck fit well on an auto carrier towed behind a U-Haul truck. The carrier kept all four wheels off the road during the trip so that the drive shaft and motor were not spinning with the rear wheels. My friend, Ev, who had finished the control board, helped me to push the truck up onto the carrier. Even with the motor installed, the truck was still fairly lightweight. The challenge, really, was driving the large U-Haul and attached auto carrier which intimidated me since I had never driven such a large load. It looked like the combination would have difficulty turning a corner or navigating narrow roads. I started out very slowly and carefully, but picked up confidence along the way.

After about three hours I arrived at the new location and backed into the driveway, again carefully. The driveway slopes up towards the garage; therefore, it was very difficult off-loading the truck. My wife, Karen, and I were not able to push the truck "uphill" off the carrier. She called her office and luckily two co-workers agreed to stop by the house during their lunch hour. I got the easy job – sitting in the truck to steer and brake while they pushed the truck off the carrier. With the truck safely in the garage (yes, the brakes worked well as the truck rolled off the carrier), I began to anticipate adding the batteries to the truck.

Chapter 8

Batteries and Power Wiring

Battery Installation

I finally decided to order the batteries in October 1995. This step was not done lightly – the batteries alone cost almost $2000, but can be expected to last four or five years. The batteries were delivered by truck about noon on a Friday. The truck driver was nice enough to help me unload them into the garage. This was a good deal for me since the batteries weigh about seventy pounds each and I am not a very big guy. After lifting three of them, I was pretty worn out. The driver was, of course, curious about what I was doing with twenty T-145 Trojan deep cycle batteries at my home. So I gave him the fifteen minute tour of the truck. I have given that tour a number of times and I really enjoy explaining the novelty of the vehicle.

As soon as the driver left, I began to install the batteries. Ever since the battery box support steel had been welded into the truck, I had wondered if it had really been measured, cut, and installed properly. I did not want to go back to welding at this stage in the project.

Luckily, they all fit as planned. It only took me about thirty minutes to put the twenty batteries in place. I was exhausted afterwards, but extremely satisfied. The four batteries up front were the most difficult. I had to lift them up and over the front grille and into the battery box where the radiator had been located. The installation of these batteries was accomplished with much grunting and groaning on my part.

I took much care at this stage because it is possible to put each battery in the wrong way. The terminals should be lined up for easy wiring of the battery pack. Luckily, in preparation, I had taken some battery photos during my visit to Bob in July. I checked these photos constantly to make sure my batteries were aligned just like his.

Power Wiring

The next step was to wire the battery pack together and to wire the battery pack to the motor, controller, and contactors. This proved to be a big job which took me about six weeks to complete. Due to work and travel, I was only able to put in about eight hours a week on this job. Additionally, I needed to take frequent breaks to warm up since the November weather was getting very cold. The garage kept me out of the cold wind, but not the cold temperatures.

The cable (not wire) used for this step is 2/0 welding cable that is about ½ inch in diameter with lots of copper to carry the high current from the batteries. This current can be as high as 400 amps or more, if you really have the "pedal to the metal." Because of its thickness, the power wiring requires a special crimping tool to get good, solid crimps on the connectors. Poor crimps can degrade the performance of the vehicle. Luckily Bob had a crimping tool which I rented for the next six weeks. The local tool rental stores did not carry this tool and, in fact, did not know what I was talking about as I described what I needed.

FIGURE 18. A Trojan T-145 battery and prepared power cable before installation.

Cutting the Cable

Unlike the smaller control wiring, precise measuring is required before cutting this cable. The cable is not very flexible, so if the length is too long, the cable will not fit in place easily. Each component, such as the controller, connected to this cable is in a bolted down position, unable to move to compensate for an inaccurate cut. Also, if the cable between batteries is too long, it could put excessive stress on the battery terminals. In addition, if the cable is cut too short it can not be used. I, therefore, tried to be pretty careful because this cable is too expensive to discard due to a cutting error.

The actual process of preparing this cable starts with measuring and cutting the cable to a precise length. Most of the battery to battery connections are the same length. This cutting is done with a special cable cutter, available at most hardware stores and not very expensive. Next, a short length of insulation is removed off each end to just make room for the special cable connector, or lug. The lug is then crimped on with the special crimping tool, which is about thirty inches long to provide extra leverage. Next, heat shrink tubing is installed where the lug joins the cable insulation. This gives the cable a finished look and provides extra safety by covering any exposed copper. The heat shrink tubing is put on with a heat gun, available through a tool rental store. Lastly, protective rubber boots are slipped over the lugs onto the cable. These boots cover the lug connections after the cable is installed, as an added safety feature.

Bob's recommendation was to cut the long lengths first so that if you do make a cutting mistake, you can still use that cable to make shorter lengths. Of course, I foolishly did not follow his advice. The short lengths for connecting batteries were the easiest for me to do first and could be done inside in the warmth! The long lengths required a lot of work in the garage under the vehicle, making sure the cable would reach from the rear battery boxes to the engine compartment. Additionally, I found I could bring the short lengths and tools on my overnight business trips

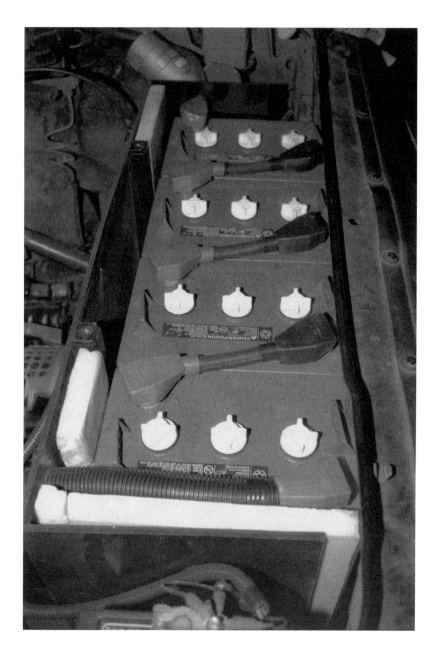

FIGURE 19. The four batteries installed in the front battery box, in the engine compartment. The short power cables are shown with a protective rubber "boot" over the connector at each end.

and work on them in the hotel room at night. Luckily I did not ruin any cable because of ignoring his advice.

Working Under the Truck

The two longer length cables proved to be a big challenge. These cables run underneath the truck, connecting the rear battery boxes to the front battery box and control board. Several steps were required prior to cutting this cable to length. First, holes were needed in the side of the polyethylene battery boxes to allow the cable to reach the first battery. I used a one inch hole saw with my power drill to cut through it easily. Next, I had to determine exactly where this cable would run underneath the truck. Obstacles included the drive shaft and the parking brake cable. Lastly, after cutting them to length, I prepared the cables for installation by inserting them into clear plastic tubing. One of Bob's safe design features is to use this tubing to protect the power cabling from damage due to road debris.

Bob recommended that the cables be bolted to the underside of the body every twenty inches to provide firm support. Bob provided cable clamps for this job. The best places I found were behind the bench seat and at the passenger's feet, near the transmission. I had to be very careful in drilling holes in the floor, to make sure I did not hit anything critical. For the next step I used my son and wife to help. While I lay under the truck with a clamp, nut, and washer, they would be inside the truck holding the other end of the bolt tight. Each of the two cables was bolted through the body in three places.

Thinking back to when I removed the transmission a year earlier, it seems that this type of work underneath the truck was the most difficult physically. Even with a hydraulic jack to raise the truck a little off the floor, a lift like you find at a repair shop would have made the job much easier. I was very happy to now be moving on to a less physically challenging tasks.

FIGURE 20. The two long power cables that connect the rear batteries to
the forward batteries. At this spot the cables are supported with bolts
that go through the floor of the cab.

Protection for the Batteries

The final task related to the batteries was to provide protection from road dirt, debris, and moisture. Without this protection, I would be spending time cleaning off the tops of the batteries. Bob's solution is to install a neoprene rubber mat over the top of each battery box. The installation proved to be fairly easy but extremely important for cleanliness and safety.

Bob supplied the rubber in a large sheet which I had to measure and cut to size. I used plastic rivets from the local hardware store to anchor one end of each mat to the battery box steel supports. The rubber mat, therefore, can roll out of the way for battery maintenance, but also can not slip off the truck accidentally. During maintenance, only one mat is removed at one time, keeping other batteries covered and shielded from metal tools that could cause an electrical short.

A unique feature of the mats is that the rubber is flexible and naturally bends to form airways from the batteries to the outside. During a battery charge some hydrogen gas is generated and can potentially concentrate in closed areas. These folds in the rubber provide airways for the hydrogen to escape and disperse, thus preventing a hazardous buildup. These rubber mats proved to be one of the simpler conversion ideas that I got from Bob, but certainly they are one of the most important contributions to the safety and cleanliness of the truck.

FIGURE 21. Top photo: The neoprene mats over the rear battery boxes.
Bottom photo: Mats rolled back for maintenance on the batteries.

Chapter 9

Charging Circuit

On-board Wiring

The last big project left was to install the wiring needed for charging the batteries. Bob's design called for the charger to plug into the same place where the S-10 would take in gasoline. I thought this was a rather humorous but convenient choice. It is certainly easier to open the small filler door than to open the hood for a charge.

A drawback of this location, however is that the charging wires must accommodate the tilt bed feature. The charging wires could easily be ripped out as the bed is tilted up for maintenance. Therefore, the wires had to run all the way to the rear of the vehicle to where the bed is hinged. From that point, one of the two wires runs along the frame to battery number one and the other wire continues to the engine compartment to battery number twenty. All of the wire is housed inside a plastic loom for protection. I installed this wiring during the first weekend in January. Luckily, we were having a very early January thaw, so with the temperature in the forties I was able to keep at it and finish in one day.

I was warned by a story Bob told me about one of his customers who also converted a Chevy S-10. This owner's truck suffered a severe arcing at the charging connection when he drove the truck through a large puddle of water. The charging connection is just in front of the rear wheel and therefore can catch a lot of water splashing up from the tire. This connection is always "hot" since it is connected directly across the battery pack. A solution is to put a protective cover over the charging connection to keep it dry. For the first six months of driving I only drove in dry weather, because I did not have a good idea of what to use for a cover. Finally, I installed a cover using the bottom of a clear plastic soda bottle with some Velcro to hold it on. It seems to work very well and is easy to remove.

Charger Hookup

There are several options available when choosing a charger. Bob supplied me with a Lester off-board charger. You can also purchase an on-board charger that is mounted permanently on the truck, in case you want to charge away from home. I do not know how much my charger weighs, but I can just barely lift it off the floor. Obviously it is not something you want to carry around in the back of the truck in case there is an opportunity to charge. The charger can use either 120 volt or 220 volt power. Bob recommended that I use 220 volts, to get a faster charge and to keep the batteries healthy. I did not have 220 volt power in the garage, but luckily I did have it in the laundry room next to the garage.

We use a gas dryer in the laundry room which leaves the 220 volt outlet unused. At this point I had learned a lot about automotive wiring but I did not want to assume that I also knew very much about house wiring. Therefore, I called a local electrician to come out to the house. Within about an hour he was able to rotate the receptacle so that it pointed out to the garage instead

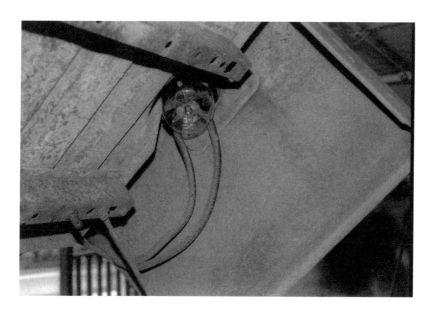

FIGURE 22. Top photo: The charging receptacle inside the gas filler door. Bottom photo: The plastic splash cover over the back side of the charging connection (the bed is tilted up in the photo).

of inside. The connection also required a different type of socket which I had already bought at the hardware store and he was able to install that for me.

Extension Cord

The last problem I found with the charging setup was the distance from the truck to the charging receptacle. The extension cord that came with the charger was too short by about eight feet. Although I looked for alternatives, I was not able to find a pre-made 220 volt extension with the proper plug and receptacle configuration. An air conditioner extension cord could work but it was "out of season" in January. I decided to buy the cable and hardware to make up an extension cord, and shopping around saved me a lot on these supplies. At an electrical supply shop I would have paid about $45, but at the local hardware store (the one that has been there for 80 years and stocks one of everything) I got what I needed for $20.

FIGURE 23. The truck charging in the garage with the Lester charger plugged into the charging receptacle.

Chapter 10

First Drive

Last Checks

Finally, I did not have any more excuses. On a Monday morning in mid January I decided to take the plunge. Several weeks earlier I had registered the truck and installed the license plate. I had been concerned about how easy the registration would be; would it make any difference that the truck was electric powered? The people at the AAA office, however, did not care that the vehicle was electric, and I did not see any questions on the forms that even asked about the engine type. So I paid the standard registration fee and was on my way.

I still wished Bob was there to do an inspection of the truck before this first drive. I felt there was probably some fatal flaw in the way I had wired the truck. I wondered if the truck would just sit there and do nothing, or worse, I feared that something catastrophic might happen to cause damage and injury. Because the batteries are delivered with a "surface charge," the first charge only took about fifty minutes. I watched until the charging current had dropped to five amps, and then I stopped it, just as Bob had suggested.

It Worked!

After making a last minute check to see that everything was closed, secured, and bolted down, I jumped in and turned the key. Out of habit I gave the ignition switch an extra turn to "turn over" the engine. But I immediately realized that this was unnecessary. Once the key is turned just two clicks, the truck is ready to go. The ignition switch engages the primary contactor. Pushing the accelerator pedal engages the secondary contactor when the potbox arm moves. When I turned the key, the vacuum pump, which serves the power brakes, kicked on. It makes a noticeable racket so I waited a few seconds until it turned off. I then pushed the accelerator and the truck started moving. This happened without the customary engine noise of an internal combustion engine. At first it was disorienting because the movement was not accompanied by the normal engine growl.

I was not sure where I was going as I left the garage. Bob had suggested a five mile drive to start, but I had not planned out a route. I was nervous about whether the truck would work as advertised, and whether I would be able to get back home, no matter how far I went. In the back of my mind, I knew that there was not an electric vehicle "mechanic" out there to help me.

It was a perfect winter day to get out. The roads were finally dry after record snowfalls. It was only January 15th and we already had twenty more inches of snowfall than in an average winter. I was also grateful that the temperature was about forty-five degrees because I had not yet installed a heater. As I turned out of the driveway and down the road, everything seemed okay. I decided to go around the block and get right back home. I did not want to push the truck (or my luck) the first time out. I also knew that the truck was not yet inspected and I was sure to run into the police if I went too far.

As I finished going around the block my confidence started to rise. Since I had not had my ritual cup of coffee yet that morning, I decided to drive down to the local McDonald's drive through window. This, however, would get me out onto one of the major business streets. I had my fingers crossed that I would not see a police car, and that the truck would continue to drive well. As I drove to McDonald's, I thought about what the truck would look like to other drivers. I realized that they would merely see an ordinary ten year-old faded blue S-10 pickup driving past. No big deal, nothing special.

The drive through McDonald's went well. I was somewhat surprised that the McDonald's drive through window employees did not notice that my truck coasted in and out without making any noise. But then again, that was all I was thinking about – the truck's unique source of power.

First Impressions

On the way home the novelty started to wear off, and I started to notice some things which I did not like about the way the truck was driving. One problem was the steering wheel; it was not lined up properly after the conversion from power to manual steering. I had to turn the wheel considerably to the left to make the tires to go straight. That would be a fairly simple adjustment.

The other problem was that the truck was very sluggish on hills. I had not noticed this sluggishness on the drive to McDonald's because the roads are mostly downhill. On the drive back, however, I was not able to get above twenty-five miles per hour on moderate grades, and it took quite a while to get up to that speed. On flat grades, the truck seemed to do fine, and if I had a run on a flat grade before a hill, I could build up speed. After talking with Bob about the problem, I learned that my controller was limiting my acceleration since it has a current limit of 400 amps. One solution is to get a controller that has a limit of 500 amps, but this costs another $500, so it had to wait.

By the time I got back home, I had driven four miles. I felt a big relief when I finally reached the garage and turned off the truck.

I immediately started to recharge the batteries in hopes of taking another drive in the afternoon. My son was very excited about the truck and had asked me to pick him up after school with the truck. This charge took much longer. The first charge had started at a thirteen amp rate, but this one started at twenty-six amps. It took about three and a half hours for the charge to get down to five amps, leaving me plenty of time for another drive.

First Problem

After the charge I left to pick up my son at his after school program. The drive went fine until I was halfway back home. As I was going down a slight downgrade, I took my foot off the accelerator to coast. Every other time I had done this the ammeter would drop to zero as the potbox arm returned to its off position, but this time the ammeter continued to register about 100 amps. I was confused about what this meant. At first I thought it could be something wrong with the transmission, so I checked to see if it was in the proper gear. I shifted into neutral but could not get back into second or third gear. The gears grinded loudly as I tried. Now I started to panic. I was coasting down a major business street with an electric vehicle that would not go into gear. I finally got to my corner and had enough momentum to make the turn and then pull over to the side of the road. After stopping and turning off the truck, I immediately tried to turn it back on. To my surprise, nothing happened. The truck appeared to be dead. Now I really started to panic. I put on the emergency flashers and started to think.

My first thought was to get to a phone as fast as possible, call AAA for a tow truck, and get the truck into the garage where I could think clearly, but I finally decided to open the hood and take a look. I immediately found the problem. The accelerator cable had curled up in the last few inches before it connects to the potbox. This curl was enough to prevent the potbox arm from reaching the off position even with my foot off the accelerator. This also explained why I was not able to restart the truck.

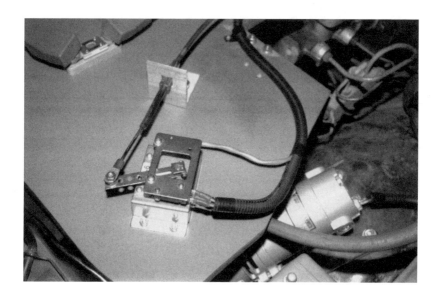

FIGURE 24. The Curtis PB-6 potbox on the control board, showing the connection to the accelerator cable which I installed, at first, improperly.

The potbox is what signals the secondary contactor to close. With the potbox still "on" it was not able to send that signal. So I straightened out the accelerator cable and got back in the truck.

The truck turned on normally, went into second gear, and started to move. I had my fingers crossed that the accelerator cable would behave during the few miles left to get home. As I turned into the driveway, I was very relieved, but also very satisfied with my performance. I had experienced my first roadside emergency and figured it out by myself. I do not think I was ever able to do that with any of my gasoline powered cars. My experience in putting the electric truck together made all the difference in being able to spot the problem.

Approximately three weeks later, I finally figured out why the accelerator cable continued to stick. I found that by bolting the cable tightly to the potbox arm, the cable did not have freedom of movement during acceleration and deceleration, which resulted in binding up. I decided to use a double nut and lockwasher scheme so that the cable could swivel freely as the potbox arm moved. This solution worked fine. I had been considering the addition of a spring to help pull the potbox arm back to the "home" position, but this proved to be unnecessary.

State Inspection

Within a week of the first drive I knew I had to get this truck inspected. But I also knew that all of my twelve volt systems were not working. The windshield wipers, radio, brake lights, and ventilation fan seemed to work fine. The headlights and horn, however, did not work at all. It seemed unlikely that the horn and headlight bulbs were all broken. The Chilton repair manual includes a very basic electrical schematic, but did not include enough detail for me to figure out the problem. I also checked the fuses, which appeared to be okay. So I took the truck to a local shop that advertised electrical repair.

The automotive electrician was fascinated with the truck and seemed very enthusiastic about getting the chance to work on it. I explained the problem to him and offered a clue where to look. I suspected that the wire "spaghetti" left over from the removal of the internal combustion engine may contain something important. He agreed that some key wires were probably cut but were still accessible since I had not completely removed them. I was very thankful that I had not indiscriminately ripped out this wire bundle just to make the truck look neat.

I got the truck back that same day with the lights and horn in working order. The electrician had restored the severed wiring in only about one hour of work. The truck had also passed inspection, so I drove home in a legal electric vehicle for the first time. He told me about several items that he overlooked during the inspection but which should be fixed soon. The tires needed replacement, the heater did not work (I had not yet installed the electric heater), and the backup lights did not work. I would find out months later (as I got ready for the next year's inspection) that the backup light wiring was also missing and required installation. I was certainly learning a lot about automotive systems.

Chapter 11

Driving Impressions

Driving Habits

In the eighteen months since the first drive, I have driven the truck about 2,000 miles. Usually I use it for errands around town, mostly on weekends. Bob indicated that the batteries would take between thirty and fifty charging cycles to break in fully. During this time, I have charged the batteries about fifty times. The charges typically last overnight, about ten to twelve hours, but even short charges of four to six hours during the day can add enough energy to drive quite a few miles around town.

Driving the truck is a little different than driving a gasoline vehicle. I need to plan my routes more carefully. Because of the hills in town, I find myself taking the flattest roads possible. There are some main streets where I could get stuck at a stop light on an uphill grade, and although the truck can handle the grade, the speed would be slow enough to annoy other drivers. Luckily, I have alternate routes that only add a few minutes to my travel time.

I also find myself doing a lot of coasting to save energy. Even with a slight down grade, the truck coasts very well. The drive train spins freely with my foot off the pedal, unlike a gasoline car. The truck is also very heavy and therefore builds up quite a bit of momentum going down hill. This means that I have to pump the brakes occasionally to prevent a runaway truck that cannot be stopped.

Performance

Another interesting difference is that an electric vehicle performs differently as the battery voltage decreases when the truck is driven. After a charge, the battery voltage may be as high as 130 or more (for a 120 volt vehicle), but it could be as low as 120 volts or less when it is ready for a charge. This decrease in voltage has a big effect on vehicle performance. Immediately after a charge the truck seems very peppy and ready to go, but near the end of its driving range with a lower battery voltage, the truck seems to almost labor when going up hills. It loses that peppy feeling. I therefore drive the truck very conservatively to prolong the higher voltage levels.

This experience contrasts with that of driving a car with an internal combustion engine. The energy delivered by gasoline does not decrease as the gas tank level goes down. The octane rating of the gasoline with a full tank is the same as the octane rating of the last gallon. The energy level does not drop until you run out of gas.

Another difference with the truck is how it behaves at a stop sign or light. When I first stop the truck, I can hear the vacuum pump working to restore the vacuum pressure for the brakes. After ten seconds or so, the vacuum pump goes off, which results in complete silence (unless the radio is playing). The first few times I drove the truck this silence was very unnerving. Because I was used to an idling internal combustion engine, it felt like the truck had "stalled." Actually, though, the truck is turned on and waiting for the accelerator to say "go." One great advantage, of course, is that at a stop light the truck is not using energy to idle.

Certainly, the major difference with an electric vehicle is the distance it can cover between charges, compared to the range of a gasoline vehicle. My Geo Metro can go up to 400 miles on one full tank of gas – ten gallons at forty miles per gallon. The truck, however, would need to be charged daily if I used it regularly. The maximum distance I have driven on one charge is fifty-five miles. During that drive I was trying for maximum range by staying on flat roads where possible and by keeping a very light foot on the accelerator pedal.

During the summer months I average about forty to forty-five miles per charge. This range would be better except for several factors. The main reason is that the area is hilly and I can not always find a flatter route. The batteries work very hard to pull the heavy truck up these hills. I can easily draw 300-400 amps going twenty-five miles per hour up a hill. On the other hand, the truck can easily cruise on a flat grade at thirty-five miles an hour using only 100-150 amps.

Another reason for the low range is that I routinely go seven to ten days without charging because I am not driving every day. I may drive the truck six miles to run errands one day and then not drive it for five days while I am out of town on business. Bob said that the batteries may lose one percent of charge a day while sitting idle. So if the truck sits for ten days between charges, I could be losing about five miles of range.

Operating Cost

The cost of charging the truck has been very reasonable. I checked the total cost by recording the amperage hourly during a twelve hour charge. The total DC (direct current) ampere-hours put into the truck added up to about 137. The charger charges at about 135 DC volts, which is the battery pack voltage at the end of a charge. Using these two figures, the total energy charged into the truck was about 18.5 kilowatt hours (137 ampere-hours times the 135 volts). Assuming that the charger is only about ninety percent efficient in converting AC (alternating current) power to DC power, the batteries actually use about twenty-one kilowatt hours during a charge. My local utility company charges about six cents per kilowatt hour. So my cost for a charge is about $1.26 (twenty-one kilowatt hours times $0.06). If I can get forty miles of driving out of that charge, then my operating cost (for just the electricity) is about three cents per mile driven ($1.26 divided by forty miles).

If we add in the cost of the batteries, this drives up the operating cost significantly. I should be able to get 500 charging cycles out of the batteries. If I can continue to get forty miles out of each charge then I will get about 20,000 miles out of these batteries. At a cost of almost $2,000, the batteries contribute ten cents per mile to the operating cost. So overall, just accounting for the batteries and electricity, the operating cost is thirteen cents per mile. This is much higher than the cost of gasoline for a conventional vehicle, but the electric vehicle has much lower maintenance costs. This is because the electric vehicle has few moving parts that need upkeep, other than the tires, brakes, transmission, wheel bearings, etc.

Reliability

The truck has been exceptionally reliable for me. Except for one problem with the original twelve volt battery, I have never been unable to start up the truck and drive away. My first twelve volt battery failed after fifteen months in the truck. Because of the way that this battery is charged, I will probably have a problem with the new one also. The only time that the DC to DC converter is charging the twelve volt battery is when the truck is running. Since I only drove the truck about 1,000 miles over the first year, this battery spent a lot of time sitting idle in the garage. The result was that I had to recharge this battery several times using an external charger, and finally it failed while I was out driving. When the battery failed, the truck shut down because the contactors on the control board need twelve volt power to close. In this case, four miles from home, I needed a tow truck. Since I replaced the battery, I have not had any further problems.

The only other time that I had to stop on the roadside was due to the problem with the potbox that I had on the first day that I drove the truck. I told that story in the chapter about my first drive. Luckily, this problem only temporarily stopped the truck, and I was able to drive home.

Since most of my driving is on short trips in town, the truck has a significant emissions advantage over a gasoline vehicle. When I take my Geo on a short trip, the catalytic converter does not start working efficiently until it is at a high temperature, which could take as long as five minutes. During that five minutes, the emissions are much higher than when the car is warmed up. The auto companies are trying to correct that problem and probably will soon. An electric vehicle, however, does not require that warm-up time. This advantage certainly makes an electric vehicle a good choice for short trips around town when tail pipe emissions are a consideration.

Summary

So, I have been very satisfied with the vehicle based on cost, reliability, and emissions considerations. The operating cost over the life of this first battery pack will be very acceptable to me. The truck has also been very reliable. Most of the reliability is due to Bob's excellent design of the conversion. Some of the reliability is also due to my experience in implementing the conversion with Bob's help. I have a lot of confidence in being able to maintain the truck at home and address problems (which have been few) on the road. Lastly, the truck certainly meets all of my expectations in terms of emissions. I get a lot of satisfaction in being able to charge at home rather than filling up at a gas station.

Chapter 12

Routine Maintenance

Just as a gasoline powered vehicle requires routine maintenance, an electric vehicle also has some regular checks. Tire pressure is one of the key areas that should be checked regularly. On my truck, I can use higher than normal pressures, as I will discuss in the next chapter. I try to check these pressures several times a month to make sure I am using the best pressure. These higher pressures are important to help reduce rolling resistance and thereby increase the truck's range on a charge.

The batteries also require some routine maintenance. One of these checks is the battery water level, because the water level goes down as some of the water evaporates during operation and charging. The manufacturer cautions that if the water level goes below the top of the lead plates, the batteries could be damaged. I have been checking the level and adding water about four times a year. Each time, I have added a little more than one gallon of water, in total, to the twenty batteries. A key point to remember is that distilled water, only, is added to the batteries, rather than regular tap water. The minerals in tap water will damage the batteries if added.

Other checks include battery voltage and battery specific gravity. These checks can give indications if a battery is performing worse than other batteries and is starting to fail. I use my multimeter to check the voltage of each battery and record the results for future reference. I do this at the same time I add water because it is easy to remember that way. There should not be any reason to check individual battery voltages after each charge as long as the vehicle seems to be performing well.

The specific gravity readings also are an indication of battery health. These readings indicate the "strength" of the sulfuric acid electrolyte inside each battery cell (three cells for each battery in my vehicle). A battery hydrometer is used to measure the specific gravity. I have only measured the specific gravities several times, since the battery voltages seem to be consistent and normal. A yearly check for new and healthy batteries is probably frequent enough. Again, as with the battery voltages, it is a good idea to write down the specific gravity readings to develop a history for each battery.

Chapter 13

Upgrading the Vehicle

New Tires

In the first year I made some improvements to the truck that have
made a big difference in its overall performance. The first
improvement was to put on new tires. The truck's original tires
did not match and were very worn. I had heard about "low
rolling resistance" tires made especially made for electric
vehicles. In hopes of doing all I could to maximize range, I
called two major tire manufacturers to see what was available.
Only Goodyear seemed eager to talk about and sell these tires.

They connected me with an engineer named Bill Egan (see
Appendix D). Bill was very pleasant on the phone and helped
me find the right tires. He asked me all about my truck including
the total weight and weight distribution. I did not know the
truck's weight, but he needed that to make a recommendation.
The only scale I knew about is at the local trash transfer station
where the garbage trucks are weighed. This scale was about ten
miles away and would constitute my longest drive yet since this
was only one month after my first drive and I was still trying to
gradually break in the batteries.

The truck turned out to be very heavy (over 4000 pounds). I called Bill back with the weights, and he recommended the Goodyear Conquest tire which has relatively low rolling resistance. This tire is not made specially for electric vehicles but its low rolling resistance made it a good choice for the truck. I went down to the Goodyear dealer with the tire information. I fully expected these tires would require a special order, but the tires were in stock and they put them on that same day.

Happily, the truck handled much better with the new tires. I dramatically increased their air pressures with the air pump as soon as I got home. Bill Egan had given me some guidelines on air pressures to further reduce the rolling resistance of the tires. These were well above the normal recommended pressures. For instance, he recommended fifty psi in the rear. He said that the tire could easily handle the pressure. In the front, however, the limit was about forty-one psi. This limit, he said, was to make sure that enough of the tire would make contact with the pavement for positive steering control. Positive steering control sounded very good to me. Any increase in range, however, would probably be too small to accurately measure.

New Controller

The next big improvement was to replace the controller. I continued to be unhappy with the truck's acceleration and climbing ability. As I mentioned before, Bob said it was partly due to the controller which limited the motor current to 400 amps. The manufacturer, Curtis, had started shipping a newer model which allowed 500 amps and promised a smoother acceleration. The trade-in cost was $500, much less than a new controller. Despite my wife's claim that the truck was no more than a money pit, I ordered the new controller from Bob.

After the controller arrived in May 1996, I had to wait a month to install it. I delayed the installation because I had my first appointment to demonstrate the truck. My son's fourth grade class wanted to see the truck as part of their semester long study of energy. I did not want to risk disabling the truck before I had a chance to show it to them. Thankfully, the demonstration went very well – the kids and the teachers had lots of questions, and I felt like a bit of an expert as I fielded them.

Adding to my confidence, the new controller went in very easily. All of the connections were the same as the old controller. Because of my experience in building the truck, it only took about three hours to complete the installation. This time was mostly spent drilling new mounting holes in the control board because the new controller was slightly larger than the old one. On the first drive I was amazed at the difference in performance. As expected, the truck accelerated up hills much better than with the old controller. The acceleration also seemed to be much smoother than with the original controller. I enjoyed driving the truck even more than before. The downside of this improved performance, though, was that it cost extra battery energy to go faster up the hills.

Electric Heater

I did not install the heater the previous winter as I was finishing the conversion because by the time the truck was ready to run, I was tired of working out in the cold garage. At the time, I was willing to put up with driving the truck without a heater. Luckily, the shop that did the state inspection overlooked the missing heater; in Pennsylvania, a vehicle is supposed to have a heated defrost. Because I could not expect to be so lucky again, I decided to make the heater installation a summer project. However, this did not happen as planned because the summer months were so full of fun summer stuff. The heater did not go in until the fall when the weather was already getting cold again.

Surprisingly, the heater turned out to be one of the most frustrating jobs on the truck. After several hours of struggle, I finally gave up trying to remove the old heater core. Some of the fasteners were in impossible locations for normal tools in the hands of a novice mechanic. In addition, working upside down under the dash board was very uncomfortable. Finally, I took the truck to a repair shop to have the heater removed, and asked them to return the truck with the dash board left apart. I needed to work fast now since it was late October and the weather was cooling down quickly.

When I got the truck back into my garage, the new heater mounted into the heater box rather easily with the parts and instructions Bob had provided. The heater box is the assembly which the repair shop had removed for me. Also, since I now had a good deal of experience with wiring the truck, the heater wiring was not difficult. The most difficult part was putting the heater box back into the truck, under the dash board. Since I had not removed the heater box, I was not familiar with all the "stuff" under the dash.

Working Under the Dash

The clearance for installing the heater box under the dash was very tight. I had to push the dash up out of the way to get the heater box in place. I was afraid I would inadvertently break something. This work was tiring and frustrating while I struggled from my position on the floor under the dash. Once the heater box was in, I elected to leave several fasteners undone; these were the same ones that I was unable to remove when I started the heater job.

After the dash board was back in place I noticed a left over part from the ventilation system. I had forgotten to hook up the small hoses that supply air to the side vent windows. The only way to do that was to take the dash apart again. Well, it will just have to wait for warmer weather.

The heater and defrost seem to work well without this detail. One really good feature about the heater is that the warm air starts as soon as the heater is turned on. You do not have to wait for the engine to warm the radiator. The heater really does a nice job a removing the chill on a 15°F; the only drawback is reduced range when using the heater.

Upgrading the Suspension

At this same time, I decided to stop procrastinating about the rear suspension. Bob had told me very early in the project that I would need to add another leaf spring to the rear suspension. I cut corners by putting on the helper springs, which did not seem to help very much. The bed of the truck sat slightly low compared to the cab.

Ever since I had started to drive the truck, there was an annoying vibration during acceleration. Specifically, when passing between thirty and thirty-five miles per hour, the whole truck would shake. At speeds below thirty and above thirty-five the truck ran fairly smoothly. I always wondered if the cause was a misalignment between the motor, clutch plate, adapter plate, and transmission. Bob had emphasized how important that alignment is for a smooth running truck. I also suspected, however, that the overloaded back end contributed to the problem.

In looking for a source of extra leaf springs, I found a spring shop about twenty-five miles away. This was on the very edge of the truck's range (fifty miles round trip), however, there are some steep hills on that route. This shop could make up the springs and install them but I might not have enough charge left to get the truck back home. I had considered putting the charger in the back and recharging at their shop. Since I had not tried charging from 110 volts yet, I decided to drive my Geo to pick up the springs and bring them back for a local shop to install.

I waited at the spring shop for about an hour while the mechanic cut and bent the spring stock to the Chevy S-10 specifications. He asked me about the "offset" for the hole in the springs. I did not know what he was talking about but luckily he had a specification reference book which had this measurement. Apparently, the hole which is drilled through the spring for mounting is not exactly in the middle of the spring. This offset is critical during installation. He also included some clips to hold all of the leafs together after installation.

The same shop that removed the heater also put in the new leafs. When I picked up the truck I could immediately tell that the rear end of the truck was sitting much higher. On the drive home I also found that I had a better view of the road since the hood did not seem so high. Several days later on a longer drive, I got the truck up over thirty miles per hour. I was pleasantly surprised to find that the vibrations did not happen. The truck accelerated smoothly through thirty miles per hour and beyond. I finally felt confident that the drive train alignment was in fact done properly.

Chapter 14

Future Plans for the Truck

As with any project like this truck, there are always more improvements to be made. There are three improvements that I would like to make which could actually be done during a conversion project rather than after the truck is on the road. First, I want to install a splash shield around the motor. Bob recommended this to me, and he has one on his converted S-10. Bob used the bottom half of a plastic pail which just fits around the end of the motor and lets in air for cooling. Because I have not done this yet, I have to avoid driving on days with heavy rain and I avoid big puddles.

Another big improvement would be to install hydraulic lifters to help lift the bed. These are similar to the lifters that are used on the tailgate of a minivan. I lift the bed manually now and can do it without help, but it is very heavy; I wonder if I will want to do this five years from now as I get older. Bob's truck has these lifters, which made this operation very easy for a driver of almost any age.

Weight Reduction

The biggest improvement that I could possibly make to this truck is to reduce the weight in order to improve performance. If I could improve the range to seventy-five miles instead of forty-five, and if the acceleration and hill climbing performance were better, I would use the truck more often. My long range goal is to rely solely on an electric vehicle for transportation. Without improved truck performance, I hesitate to finally sell my Geo Metro. I am not alone in this concern for performance. It is also reflected in the GM approach to leasing its new EV1 vehicle. GM has a screening process which looks for a certain driver profile. One guideline in the profile is that the lessee also has an internal combustion engine vehicle as a backup. They apparently are not yet confident enough in the car's performance to look for people who want to rely solely on an electric vehicle.

In order to lighten the truck, I have investigated replacing body panels with lightweight materials such as fiberglass or plastic or composite. I have not, however, found any lightweight replacement body panels that are cost effective. The most promising replacement part is a "roll pan" to replace the rear bumper. The roll pan fits in the space under the tailgate and between the bed side panels. Overall, this replacement may be able to reduce weight by as much a one hundred pounds since the fiberglass roll pan only weighs a few pounds.

Battery Improvements

Obviously, the biggest opportunity for weight reduction is in the batteries. New technologies have developed since I bought my batteries, but I have only put fifty cycles (discharge and charge) on this first set of batteries. These batteries are advertised to last over 500 cycles, so I have a long ways to go to recover my initial investment. The pace of battery development, however, is accelerating, and there is a lot of progress reported in this area. New alternatives, not yet affordable, include Ni-Cad, Zinc-Air,

Nickel Metal Hydride, and others. A test of Zinc-Air batteries by a company named B.A.T. in December 1996 claimed a range of over 400 miles for a delivery truck in freezing weather. I would be very happy with just one fourth of that range. B.A.T. ran another test with a smaller vehicle in June 1997 and achieved over 1,000 miles on a single charge. These results are truly exciting for the electric vehicle industry and owners.

Several companies such as Electrosource, Inc. and Optima, are advancing lead acid battery technology. If I could get the same power from batteries that weigh half as much as my current batteries (Electrosource's Horizon batteries approach that performance), the truck would weigh 3,200 pounds rather than 4,000 pounds. The performance improvement would be dramatic, but given the economics of battery replacement, I will wait a few more years for the prices to drop. Today, it would cost about $5000 to install the Horizon batteries in my truck.

Chapter 15

What I Learned

Here is a summary of what I learned during the conversion. I offer these thoughts to anyone who is considering such a project – especially someone like myself who does not have natural mechanical and electrical talent to be able to intuitively breeze through this type of work.

First, I recommend talking to several conversion companies before diving in to a project like this. Ask lots of questions to learn what their approach is to coaching someone through the conversion, as well as learning about their vehicle design. Visit one or more of these companies to meet the owners and see their operations before selecting a partner company to help you. I was very lucky to have selected Bob Batson and EVA, but since I did not do a thorough job of screening the companies, I could easily have made a poor choice. Additionally, a prospective company can refer you to some customers who have already done a conversion. That may be one your best sources of good information in making this choice.

Consider weight at every step of the conversion. The electric vehicle's performance, both acceleration and range, is heavily dependent on the final weight after conversion. If you need to add structural members (for example, battery box supports), be sure to take into account the thickness, or gauge, of the steel. Select materials that will keep the weight down, while at the same time ensuring a safe vehicle. Additionally, look for any opportunity to remove parts that are not needed. There are lots of items required for an internal combustion engine which are unnecessary for an electric vehicle.

Establish a good "foundation" for the vehicle by upgrading the suspension and ensuring good brakes. These two automotive systems are crucial to the operation of any vehicle, and especially a heavy electric vehicle. Both of these systems can be upgraded early in the conversion process. As I found with my truck, the "stock" suspension was not strong enough, resulting in vibrations at certain speeds. Keeping the power brake feature has provided good, safe braking for the truck. It is tempting to eliminate the power brake feature to simplify the vehicle and reduce the electrical power load, but in the long run it may not be a safe decision.

Get other people to help you, especially if, like me, you do not have a lot of automotive and electrical experience. Some of the conversion jobs, such as steel fabrication and welding, were certainly way beyond my experience and skill level and I did not consider learning how to do them. Other tasks involving the brakes and suspension were ones I could have learned to do, given enough time and patience. I elected, however, to find someone who could do them well and safely. The actual work that I did was mostly confined to the control and power wiring systems. I am glad I learned how to do that work, because now I have an excellent understanding of how the truck works, and how to maintain and repair its electrical system. But even with the electrical installation, I needed some one-on-one coaching from Bob to be able to properly and safely install the wiring.

Do not cut corners with electrical safety. I relied on Bob to teach me what is important in electrical vehicle safety. I tried to follow his advice on components, materials, and installation procedures in order to build a safe vehicle. Electric vehicles are very safe when they incorporate a safe design and sound wiring installation. Try to understand how safe operation and maintenance is incorporated into the design of your vehicle.

Join an electric vehicle organization and get their newsletter to stay up to date with what's going on in the industry. One newsletter, the monthly *Current Events* newsletter of the Electric Vehicle Association (see Appendix E), is loaded with information on components, installation tips, new products, industry news, suppliers, calendar of events, electric vehicle race results, and classified advertisements. This is a great way to plug into the industry and learn something new in every issue.

Finally, the project may cost more time and money than you estimate up front. I believe this happened to me because of my inexperience with vehicles of any kind, and because the truck I purchased needed quite a bit of repair. But be patient – it will be worth it when you take your first drive.

Chapter 16

After 10,000 Miles

It is now two years since the initial publication of this book, and almost four years since I first drove this converted truck. There is enough experience to fill up a new chapter, but not enough for a whole new book!

Performance

I kept a logbook with all of the information on each charge, in terms of when the charge occurred, how long it lasted, and the finishing charge rate. This has provided very good data on range per charge. I noted in the logbook when I did a "quick" charge (less than 2 hours or so), but I did not keep complete information on those charges.

In summary, I have driven 10,270 miles on 330 charges, for an average of 31 miles per charge. This low value is mostly due to our cold winter weather which can significantly reduce the battery performance. Additionally, I live in a relatively hilly area. The batteries sometimes struggle to get the truck over these hills. The longest range that I achieved came in mid-summer when I tried to stay on level roads while driving conservatively. On that drive the truck managed 56 miles. Otherwise, the truck routinely reaches 40-45 miles per charge in the summer.

Here is a summary of the charges and range over the past four years. I have only calculated the range for full charges - charges that lasted seven hours or longer. The far right column, however, is the total miles driven for each year.

Table 1: Average Range per Charge

Season	Number of Full Charges	Average Range in Miles	Total Distance for the Year in Miles
Winter 96	2	26.5	
Spring 96	8	34.9	
Summer 96	8	43.8	
Fall 96	6	38.8	
Winter 96-97	9	30.1	1100
Spring 97	8	39.4	
Summer 97	8	39.4	
Fall 97	11	27.2	
Winter 97-98	13	28.8	1600
Spring 98	8	30.4	
Summer 98	20	40.6	
Fall 98	28	35.5	
Winter 98-99	24	25.7	3310
Spring 99	31	32.5	
Summer 99	24	41.2	
Fall 99	31	33.0	
Winter 99	14	26.8	4260
Total			10,270

Breakdown Information

In chapter 11 I mentioned two times when I had a breakdown on the road. Since then, I have only had one further breakdown. In July 1999 the truck shut down just as I was pulling into the parking lot where I work. I had enough momentum to slide into a parking space. I sure was lucky on the timing.

Because of the sudden nature in which the truck shut down, I suspected a fuse, but did not know which one. There are two large 500 amp fuses in the battery circuit under the bed and a 300 amp fuse on the control board. Any one of these could have caused this sudden shutdown. I tilted up the bed and visually inspected the two 500 amp fuses and they appeared to be ok. They are protected inside a clear plastic tube, so it is easy to see their condition. The 300 amp fuse on the control board, however, looked abnormal. Using a multimeter, I verified that this fuse was blown. I was concerned that I did not know why this happened.

I called Bob Batson to get some direction on what to do about this. He was right there when I called. He suggested that this fuse, being a 300 amp time delay fuse, had just gotten tired after more than three years of absorbing large current surges. He did not expect that some other problem in the truck had caused the fuse to blow. So Bob's recommendation was to bypass this fuse temporarily until he could send another fuse in the mail. This 300 amp fuse is a backup to the two 500 amp fuses, so the truck is still fully protected with the 300 amp fuse by bypassed.

So, I only lost use of the truck for several hours while I did the troubleshooting and then bypassed the fuse. The new fuse arrived several days later and the truck was back to normal. In summary, breakdowns have not caused very much downtime in four years. All three breakdowns combined resulted in less than one lost day of driving. I am very pleased with this record.

Watering Routine

Since I am now driving the truck more frequently, I am also watering the batteries more frequently. I initially scheduled this maintenance for every 500 miles of driving. But in the third year I started to find several cells with low water level (water level just below the top of the plates) after 500 miles. I finally realized that rather than scheduling the water addition for every 500 miles, I should be scheduling it based on number of charges. In the middle of the winter, 500 miles might come after 20 charges, while in the summer it might come after only 12 charges. I have settled into a frequency of adding water every 14-15 charge cycles. I am no longer finding cells with uncovered plates when it is time for watering.

The watering routine is taking about an hour and a half. Some of this time is due to opening up the bed and then putting it back together. Also, each watering uses between one and one and a half gallons of distilled water.

Improvements Made

I have made several improvements to the truck in the past several years. The first one is a soft naugahyde bed cover. I wanted to make the truck more aerodynamic (it's a square S-10) and hopefully this helped a little bit. I also put on an air dam under the front bumper to make that part of the truck more aerodynamic. The new GM electric S-10 also has an air dam which apparently reaches all the way back under the engine compartment. I tried to find out information about this from my local Chevy dealer but they could not identify it in their computer system.

To help address the weight problem with this truck, I removed the rear bumper and installed a fiberglass roll pan. I estimate that this improvement may have eliminated 75-80 pounds, but I did not weigh the removed bumper. This should also improve the aerodynamics since the bumper no longer sticks out on both sides of the bed. The roll pan does hit the rear battery box when the bed is tilted, so I have to remove one set of bolts which allows the roll pan to tilt out of the way.

In the winter and spring of 1998, I became concerned that the truck's range was not as good as the previous year. In hindsight, some this range problem was due to the winter effect. But it did appear that 1997 was a better year for the truck. In one of the monthly Current Events newsletters I read about a product called Power Pulse which could help to cure and prevent a situation called sulfation in lead-acid batteries. I did not know if my batteries were suffering from sulfation, but it sounded like a reasonable explanation. The newsletter article sounded very promising based on using the Power Pulse product on vehicles like mine. These vehicles had been inactive for many months and the batteries had sulfated.

I decided to go ahead and install Power Pulse in hopes of getting better performance. I needed to install four Power Pulse units - one for each battery box. The total cost was about $450. They installed very easily - about thirty minutes per unit. I installed these units in May 98, and immediately saw an increase in range per charge. In hindsight, however, this is also the time of year when the batteries are warming up to summertime temperatures. I always see increased range that time of year. So, I am not sure exactly how much benefit these units have been. The truck did experience greater range per charge for the balance of 1998 than it did in 1997. This also may have been due to my increasing experience in how to manage the truck during each charge cycle, as well as my increasing use of short charges (30-60 minutes) in between the long charges.

I had hoped to make further weight reductions in the truck but I have not found any cost effective ways to do that. I tried to find a fiberglass bed to replace the truck's rusting bed. I managed to find one model, but the manufacturer said that it would probably weigh more than my current bed since it is heavily reinforced.

I think that the best hope for weight reduction is to install lighter batteries, but those appear to be very expensive.

Next Steps

Finally, I will mention my thoughts on what is next for this vehicle and my driving habits. I have ordered solar panels to install over the bed. I thought about this for a long time, especially the costs and benefits. I decided that the panels would not pay off financially during the lifetime of this vehicle, but they would be a fun addition. Also, I am a technology instructor, so the truck will become an interesting piece of lab equipment.

In deciding which solar panels to buy, I tried to meet two criteria. One, I wanted to panels to cover the bed (about 30 square feet) and therefore double as the bed cover. Two, the combined panel voltage, when connected in series, must be high enough to charge the batteries. It was difficult to find panels that met these criteria. The only one I found is made by Solarex and is the model MX-30, which puts out 30 watts of power. Nine of these panels will almost exactly cover the bed. The series voltage is about 144 to 150 volts, which should be enough for charging.

At best, the panels will add about three miles of driving range on one sunny day. If the panels are exposed to six hours of full sun in one day, and the nine panels put out 270 watts, the panels will add about one and a half kilowatt-hours to the batteries. This energy is about eight percent of the battery capacity and translates into about three miles of driving. This is not a great addition, but over a month it will add up and maybe allow me to avoid a battery charge.

Another big event is the eventual battery replacement. I am planning on this replacement in the summer of 2001, when the truck will have about 18,000 miles and the batteries will have about 600 charge cycles. I have researched other batteries that would help to reduce the overall truck weight. Those batteries are out there, but they appear to be very expensive. One example is GM's Ovonic nickel metal hydride battery which is now installed in GM's EV-1 car. These batteries would reduce my truck's weight by 600-700 pounds. The cost to install them, however, is almost $30,000. Therefore, I plan to install a new set of Trojan T-145 batteries for $2,000, unless a better alternative appears by 2001.

Lastly, I would like to further reduce my dependence on a backup gasoline vehicle. I drive my car about once a week when I have a trip which exceeds the truck's range. I also occasionally use the car when I do not properly manage the truck's state of charge. I may need to run some errands in the evening after using up the battery charge in the daytime (and then forgetting to plug in as soon as I drive into the garage). This is a continual learning process. Maybe I should just sell my car and learn the hard way (then borrow my wife's car!).

Appendix A: Costs

Conversion Costs

Type	Cost
Truck purchase and removal of internal combustion engine and related systems	$1,500
Automotive repair costs (brakes, new tires, etc.)	$820
Fabrication and welding of battery box steel supports and tilt bed hinges	$1,245
Machining (transmission, adapter plate, misc. parts)	$85
Conversion Parts (motor, batteries, controller, etc.)	$8,940
Electrical supplies (wiring, connectors, loom, etc.)	$205
Hardware	$55
Tool purchase	$260
Tool rental (crimping tool, heat gun)	$115
Miscellaneous	$105
Grand Total	$13,330

Top Twelve Most Expensive Items

Item	Cost
1. 28 HP Advanced DC Motor, motor coupling, adapter plate, motor mounts (motor by itself was $1565)	$2150
2. 20 Trojan T-145 batteries	$1,900
3. Purchase of S-10 pickup, removal of engine, and delivery	$1500
4. Welding of battery box supports, bed hinge brackets, control board supports; installation of motor	$896
5. Lester off-board charger	$840
6. Polyethylene battery boxes	$754
7. Curtis 1221B controller	$740
8. New tires	$427
9. Power wiring (2/0 welding cable, lugs, heat shrink, protective tubing)	$375
10. Fabrication of steel for battery boxes	$347
11. Curtis DC/DC converter	$330
12. Vacuum system (pump, switch, gage)	$302

Appendix B: Conversion Time

Note: I have not included the work time of activities completed by outside contractors in the total. The total work time reflects the time I spent working on the truck. Also not included is the time spent finding a truck, finding a conversion company (EVA), time on the phone with Bob Batson, time spent finding parts and tools, and time spent just sitting around wondering what to do next!

Activity	Working Time	Calendar Time
Removal of internal combustion engine, exhaust system, and fuel system.	contract	1 day
Removal of transmission, preparation of adapter plate, etc.	12 hours	2.5 months
Steel fabrication	contract	1 month
Installation of battery box steel, motor, and transmission	contract	2 months
Fabrication of the control board and installation of components on the board	8 hours	2 weeks
Control wiring installation	20 hours	6 weeks
Vacuum system installation	6 hours	2 weeks
Battery installation and power wiring installation	21 hours	2 months
Charging circuit installation	8 hours	2 weeks
Finishing work and testing circuits prior to the first drive	8 hours	2 weeks
Total time (October 1995 to January 1996)	83 hours	15 months

Appendix C: Truck Specifications

Original vehicle:

1986 Chevrolet S-10 Pickup
Standard cab and standard bed
6 cylinder engine with a 5 speed transmission
Weight: approximately 2,700 lbs.

After conversion:

9" 28 HP DC motor by Advanced DC Motors of Syracuse, N.Y.
Curtis 1221B motor controller with 400 ampere limit *
Curtis 1400 DC/DC Converter
Contactors: 2 Curtis/Albright SW-200
Curtis PB-6 Potbox
20 Trojan T-145 six-volt deep-cycle batteries (120 volt system)
Power wiring: 2/0 welding cable
Vacuum system for power brakes
Tires: Goodyear Conquest, P205/75 R14
Weight: 4100 lbs. total (2300 rear, 1800 front)

* Upgraded to Curtis 1221C motor controller with 500 ampere
limit

Appendix D: Organizations and Other Resources

CALSTART Information Exchange
Website at http://www.calstart.org
This organization's website provides news and press releases for "advanced transportation technologies." Also has an industry yellow pages and an open forum.

Electric Auto Association
2710 St. Giles Lane
Mountain View, CA 94040
This organization publishes the monthly newsletter *Current Events* which is an excellent source of electric vehicle information.

Electric Vehicles of America
Bob Batson, President
P.O Box 2037
Wolfboro, NH 03894
Phone 603-569-2100

EV Information Network
Website at http://www.inc.com/users/evainc.html
This site includes EV facts and myths, costs, showroom of manufactured vehicles, how to do a conversion, and a lot more.

Goodyear Tires
Mr. Bill Egan
216-796-2715
Low rolling resistance tires

Northeast Sustainable Energy Association (NESEA)
50 Miles St.
Greenfield, MA 01301
413-774-6051
This organization runs the annual Tour de Sol race and generally fosters the use of renewable and sustainable energy.

Phoenix Chapter of the Electric Auto Association
Website at http://www.primenet.com/~evchdlr
This site includes an EV business directory, orientation on EV components, EV safety, reading list, and a lot more.

Real Goods
555 Leslie St.
Ukiah, CA 95482-5576
1-800-762-7325
They sell alternative energy products.

Appendix E: References

Environmental Books

McKibben, Bill (1989). *The End of Nature.* New York: Random House.

Rifkin, Jeremy (1990). *The Green Lifestyle Handbook.* New York: Henry Holt & Company.

Electric Vehicles

American Petroleum Institute. "Electric Vehicles Present Potentially Costly Safety Problems." Available at website http://www.api.org/news/evsafety.htm

Brant, Bob (1994). *Build Your Own Electric Vehicle.* Blue Ridge Summit, PA: TAB Books.

Center for Technology Assessment (February 26, 1997). New Study Finds Electric Cars Are Significantly Safer Than Gasoline Powered Vehicles. *CTA Website* available at http://www.icta.org

Electric Auto Association. *Current Events Newsletter.*

Gribben, Chip (no date). *Debunking the Myth of EV's and Smokestacks* [On-line]. Electric Vehicle Association of Greater Washington, D.C. *EV Information Network* website available at http://www.inc.com/users/evainc.html

Moates, Tom (Feb/March 1997). The Eternal Engine. *Mother Earth News, 160,* 42-50

Passell, Peter (May 9, 1995). Electric Cars Called Perilous to Environment. *The New York Times*, pp. A1, C4.

Perrin, Noel (1992). *Living with an Electric Car.* San Francisco: Sierra Club Books.

Prange, Shari (Apr/May 1993). Electric Car Adapters. *Home Power*, 34, 40-42.

Schaeffer, John Editor (1993). *Alternative Energy Sourcebook.* Ukiah, CA: Real Goods Trading Corporation.

Terpstra, Philip (1992). *1993 Worldwide Electric Vehicle Directory.* Tucson: Spirit Publications.

Index